UNDER THE TREE

"And over and over I tried to see
Some of us walking under the tree

.   .   .   .   .   .

And how it looks when I am there."

FROM *On the Hill*

UNDER THE TREE

Elizabeth Madox Roberts

Enlarged Edition, Illustrated by F. D. Bedford

NEW YORK   THE VIKING PRESS   MCMLVI

TO MY FATHER

SIMPSON ROBERTS

CONTENTS

CONTENTS

UNDER THE TREE

THE SKY

I saw a shadow on the ground
And heard a bluejay going by;
A shadow went across the ground,
And I looked up and saw the sky.

It hung up on the poplar tree,
But while I looked it did not stay;
It gave a tiny sort of jerk
And moved a little bit away.

And farther on and farther on
It moved and never seemed to stop,
I think it must be tied with chains
And something pulls it from the top.

It never has come down again,
And every time I look to see,
The sky is always slipping back
And getting far away from me.

THE CORNFIELD

I went across the pasture lot
When not a one was watching me.
Away beyond the cattle barns
I climbed a little crooked tree.

And I could look down on the field
And see the corn and how it grows
Across the world and up and down
In very straight and even rows.

And far away and far away—
I wonder if the farmer man
Knows all about the corn and how
It comes together like a fan.

MILKING TIME

When supper time is almost come,
But not quite here, I cannot wait,
And so I take my china mug
And go down by the milking gate.

The cow is always eating shucks
And spilling off the little silk.
Her purple eyes are big and soft—
She always smells like milk.

And Father takes my mug from me,
And then he makes the stream come out.
I see it going in my mug
And foaming all about.

And when it's piling very high,
And when some little streams commence
To run and drip along the sides,
He hands it to me through the fence.

IN MY PILLOW

When Mother or Father turns down the light,
I like to look into my pillow at night.

Some people call them dreams, but for me
They are things I look down in my pillow and see.

I saw some birds, as many as four,
They were all blue wings and nothing else more.

Without any head and without any feet,
Just blue wings flying over a street.

And almost every night I see
A little brown bowl that can talk to me,

A nice little bowl that laughs and sings,
And ever so many other things.

Sometimes they are plainer than I can say,
And while I am waking they go away.

And when nobody is coming by,
I feel my pillow all over and try

And try to feel the pretty things,
The little brown bowl and the flying wings.

MISS KATE-MARIE

And it was Sunday everywhere,
And Father pinned a rose on me
And said he guessed he'd better take
Me down to see Miss Kate-Marie.

And when I went it all turned out
To be a Sunday school, and there
Miss Kate-Marie was very good
And let me stand beside her chair.

Her hat was made of yellow lace;
Her dress was very soft and thin,
And when she talked her little tongue
Was always wriggling out and in.

I liked to smell my pretty rose;
I liked to feel her silky dress.
She held a very little book
And asked the things for us to guess.

She asked me about Who-made-y-God,
And never seemed to fuss or frown;
I liked to watch her little tongue
And see it wriggle up and down.

THE TWINS

The two-ones is the name for it,
And that is what it ought to be,
But when you say it very fast
It makes your lips say *twins,* you see.

When I was just a little thing,
About the year before the last,
I called it two-ones all the time,
But now I always say it fast.

THE WOODPECKER

The woodpecker pecked out a little round hole
And made him a house in the telephone pole.

One day when I watched he poked out his head,
And he had on a hood and a collar of red.

When the streams of rain pour out of the sky,
And the sparkles of lightning go flashing by,

And the big, big wheels of thunder roll,
He can snuggle back in the telephone pole.

THE STAR

A Song

O little one away so far,
You cannot hear me when I sing.

You cannot tell me what you are,
I cannot tell you anything.

THE BUTTERBEAN TENT

All through the garden I went and went,
And I walked in under the butterbean tent.

The poles leaned up like a good tepee
And made a nice little house for me.

I had a hard brown clod for a seat,
And all outside was a cool green street.

A little green worm and a butterfly
And a cricket-like thing that could hop went by.

Hidden away there were flocks and flocks
Of bugs that could go like little clocks.

Such a good day it was when I spent
A long, long while in the butterbean tent.

BIG BROTHER

Our brother Clarence goes to school.
He has a slate and a blue school-bag.
He has a book and a copybook
And a scholar's companion and a little slate rag.

He knows a boy named Joe B. Kirk,
And he learns about c-a-t cat,
And how to play one-two-sky-blue,
And how to make a football out of a hat.

We climb up on the fence and gate
And watch until he's small and dim,
Far up the street, and he looks back
To see if we keep on watching him.

MR. WELLS

On Sunday morning, then he comes
To church, and everybody smells
The blacking and the toilet soap
And camphor balls from Mr. Wells.

He wears his whiskers in a bunch,
And wears his glasses on his head.
I mustn't call him Old Man Wells—
No matter—that's what Father said.

And when the little blacking smells
And camphor balls and soap begin,
I do not have to look to know
That Mr. Wells is coming in.

DICK AND WILL

Our brother says that Will was born
The very day that Dickie came;
When one is four the other is,
And all their birthdays are the same.

Their coats and waists are just alike;
They have their hats together, too.
They sleep together in one bed,
And Will can put on Dickie's shoe.

But they are not the same at all;
Two different boys they have to be,
For Dick can play in Mother's room
When Will is climbing in a tree.

Or maybe Will is on the porch
To cry because he stubbed his toe,
And Dick is laughing by the gate
And watching ants go in a row.

FIREFLY

A Song

A little light is going by,
Is going up to see the sky,
A little light with wings.

I never could have thought of it,
To have a little bug all lit
And made to go on wings.

LITTLE RAIN

When I was making myself a game
Up in the garden, a little rain came.

It fell down quick in a sort of rush,
And I crawled back under the snowball bush.

I could hear the big drops hit the ground
And see little puddles of dust fly round.

A chicken came till the rain was gone;
He had just a very few feathers on.

He shivered a little under his skin,
And then he shut his eyeballs in.

Even after the rain had begun to hush
It kept on raining up in the bush.

One big flat drop came sliding down,
And a ladybug that was red and brown

Was up on a little stem waiting there,
And I got some rain in my hair.

THE PULPIT

On Sunday when I go to church
I wear my dress that's trimmed with lace.
I sit beside my mother and
Am very quiet in my place.

When Dr. Brown is reading hymns
To make the people want to sing,
Or when he preaches loud and makes
The shivery bells begin to ring,

I watch the little pulpit house—
It isn't very tall or wide—
And then I wonder all about
The little ones that live inside.

When Dr. Brown has preached enough,
And when he is about to stop,
He stands behind the little house
And shuts the Bible on the top.

I wonder if *they* sit inside,
And if *they* cook and walk up stairs.
I wonder if *they* have a cat
And say some kind of little prayers.

I wonder if *they're* ever scared
Because the bedroom lamp goes out,
And what their little dreams are like
And what *they* wonder all about.

ON THE HILL

Mother said that we could go
Up on the hill where the strawberries grow.

And while I was there I looked all down,
Over the trees and over the town.

I saw the field where the big boys play,
And the roads that come from every way,

The courthouse place where the wagons stop,
And the bridge and the scales and the blacksmith shop.

The church steeple looked very tall and thin,
And I found the house that we live in.

I saw it under the poplar tree,
And I bent my head and tried to see

Our house when the rain is over it,
And how it looks when the lamps are lit.

I saw the swing from up on the hill,
The ropes were hanging very still.

And over and over I tried to see
Some of us walking under the tree,

And the children playing everywhere,
And how it looks when I am there.

But Dickie said, "Come on, let's race";
And Will had found the strawberry place.

AUTUMN

Dick and Will and Charles and I
Were playing it was election day,
And I was running for president,
And Dick was a band that was going to play,

And Charles and Will were a street parade,
But Clarence came and said that he
Was going to run for president,
And I could run for school-trustee.

He made some flags for Charles and Will
And a badge to go on Dickie's coat.
He stood some cornstalks by the fence
And had them for the men that vote.

Then he climbed on a box and made a speech
To the cornstalk men that were in a row.
It was all about the dem-o-crats,
And "I de-fy any man to show."

And "I de-fy any man to say."
And all about "It's a big disgrace."
He spoke his speech out very loud
And shook his fist in a cornstalk's face.

THE PILASTER

The church has pieces jutting out
Where corners of the walls begin.
I have one for my little house,
And I can feel myself go in.

I feel myself go in the bricks,
And I can see myself in there.
I'm always waiting all alone,
I'm sitting on a little chair.

And I am sitting very still,
And I am waiting on and on
For something that is never there,
For something that is gone.

THE RABBIT

When they said the time to hide was mine,
I hid back under a thick grape vine.

And while I was still for the time to pass,
A little gray thing came out of the grass.

He hopped his way through the melon bed
And sat down close by a cabbage head.

He sat down close where I could see,
And his big still eyes looked hard at me,

His big eyes bursting out of the rim,
And I looked back very hard at him.

CRESCENT MOON

And Dick said, "Look what I have found!"
And when we saw we danced around,
And made our feet just tip the ground.

We skipped our toes and sang, "Oh-lo.
Oh-who, oh-who, oh what do you know!
Oh-who, oh-hi, oh-loo, kee-lo!"

We clapped our hands and sang, "Oh-ee!"
It made us jump and laugh to see
The little new moon above the tree.

THE RICHEST WOMAN IN THE WORLD

She has some tongs made out of pearl
To poke the fire and make it burn.
She pours the milk in diamond crocks
And churns the cream in a silver churn.

And when she's tired she has a stool;
It's made of jade with pearls set in it.
She sits down here and wipes her face
And gets her breath a minute.

On Saturday she stirs the cake
With gold, and when the water is hot,
She kills the hen with a golden axe
And scalds her in a golden pot.

She chops the meat with a golden knife
And cooks it in a golden skillet.
For coal she has a golden hod.
There is always a plenty to fill it.

FATHER'S STORY

We put more coal on the big red fire,
And while we are waiting for dinner to cook,
Our father comes and tells us about
A story that he has read in a book.

And Charles and Will and Dick and I
And all of us but Clarence are there.
And some of us sit on Father's legs,
But one has to sit on the little red chair.

And when we are sitting very still,
He sings us a song or tells a piece;
He sings Dan Tucker Went to Town,
Or he tells us about the golden fleece.

He tells about the golden wool,
And some of it is about a boy
Named Jason, and about a ship,
And some is about a town called Troy.

And while he is telling or singing it through,
I stand by his arm, for that is my place.
And I push my fingers into his skin
To make little dents in his big rough face.

CHRISTMAS MORNING

If Bethlehem were here today,
Or this were very long ago,
There wouldn't be a winter time
Nor any cold or snow.

I'd run out through the garden gate,
And down along the pasture walk;
And off beside the cattle barns
I'd hear a kind of gentle talk.

I'd move the heavy iron chain
And pull away the wooden pin;
I'd push the door a little bit
And tiptoe very softly in.

The pigeons and the yellow hens
And all the cows would stand away;
Their eyes would open wide to see
A lady in the manger hay,

If this were very long ago
And Bethlehem were here today.

And Mother held my hand and smiled—
I mean the lady would—and she
Would take the woolly blankets off
Her little boy so I could see.

His shut-up eyes would be asleep,
And he would look like our John,
And he would be all crumpled too,
And have a pinkish color on.

I'd watch his breath go in and out.
His little clothes would all be white.
I'd slip my finger in his hand
To feel how he could hold it tight.

And she would smile and say, "Take care,"
The mother, Mary, would, "Take care";
And I would kiss his little hand
And touch his hair.

While Mary put the blankets back
The gentle talk would soon begin.
And when I'd tiptoe softly out
I'd meet the wise men going in.

STRANGE TREE

Away beyond the Jarboe house
I saw a different kind of tree.
Its trunk was old and large and bent,
And I could feel it look at me.

The road was going on and on
Beyond to reach some other place.
I saw a tree that looked at me,
And yet it did not have a face.

It looked at me with all its limbs;
It looked at me with all its bark.
The yellow wrinkles on its sides
Were bent and dark.

And then I ran to get away,
But when I stopped to turn and see,

The tree was bending to the side
And leaning out to look at me.

PEOPLE GOING BY

Before they come I hear their talk
And hear their feet go on the walk.

Some go fast and some go slow,
And some of them I almost know.

In mornings they are going down
To see somebody in the town.

Or Mrs. Warner hurries past;
She has to go and come back fast.

She walks by quick and will not stop,
To go to the church with the cross on top.

I think she goes there every day
To take her rosary and pray.

And one of them is Mr. Jim—
And the big white dog that follows him.

And one is lame; that's Uncle Mells;
He takes off warts by mumbling words,
And he can lay on spells.

Or maybe night is almost come,
And Miss Jane Anne is going home.

And by her side walks Mr. Paul;
They go along with far-off looks
And hardly ever talk at all.

Or Murry's child comes up this way
To carry milk to poor Miss May

That lives in Wells's other house,
Or Joe is driving home his cows.

And some go fast and some go slow,
And some of them I almost know.

I can feel them almost speak to me,
When they pass by our tree.

BABES IN THE WOODS

The two little children that died long ago
Away in the woods on the top of a hill—
And a good little robin that knew all about it
Came with strawberry leaves in her bill,

To cover them up, and she kept very quiet
And brought the leaves one at a time, I think.
And some of the leaves would have little holes in them,
And some would be red and pink.

And these little Babes-in-the-Woods that were dead
Must have lain very still, and they heard all the talk
That the bees would be saying to more little bees,
And maybe they even could hear the ants walk.

And they could look out through a crack in the leaves
And see little bushes and some of the sky.
They could see robin coming with leaves in her mouth,
And they watched for her when she went by.

THE PICNIC

They had a picnic in the woods,
And Mother couldn't go that day,
But the twins and Brother and I could go;
We rode on the wagon full of hay.

There were more little girls than ten, I guess.
And the boy that is Joe B. Kirk was there.
He found a toad and a katydid,
And a little girl came whose name was Clare.

Miss Kate-Marie made us play a song
Called "Fare-you-well, says Johnny O'Brown."
You dance in a ring and sing it through,
And then some one kneels down.

She kissed us all and Joe B. Kirk;
But Joe B. didn't mind a bit.
He walked around and swung his arms
And seemed to be very glad of it.

Then Mr. Jim said he would play,
But Miss Marie, she told him then,
It's a game for her and the little folks,
And he could go and fish with the men.

Mr. Wells was there and he had a rope
To tie to a limb and make it swing.
And Mrs. Wells, Mr. Wells's wife,
Gave me a peach and a chicken wing.

And I had a little cherry pie
And a piece of bread, and after we'd played
Two other songs, I had some cake
And another wing and some lemonade.

THE CIRCUS

Friday came and the circus was there,
And Mother said that the twins and I
And Charles and Clarence and all of us
Could go out and see the parade go by.

And there were wagons with pictures on,
And you never could guess what they had inside,
Nobody could guess, for the doors were shut,
And there was a dog that a monkey could ride.

A man on the top of a sort of cart
Was clapping his hands and making a talk.
And the elephant came—he can step pretty far—
It made us laugh to see him walk.

Three beautiful ladies came riding by,
And each one had on a golden dress,
And each one had a golden whip.
They were queens of Sheba, I guess.

A big wild man was in a cage,
And he had some snakes going over his feet
And somebody said "He eats them alive!"
But I didn't see him eat.

MUMPS

I had a feeling in my neck,
And on the sides were two big bumps;
I couldn't swallow anything
At all because I had the mumps.

And Mother tied it with a piece,
And then she tied up Will and John,
And no one else but Dick was left
That didn't have a mump rag on.

He teased at us and laughed at us,
And said, whenever he went by,
"It's vinegar and lemon drops
And pickles!" just to make us cry.

But Tuesday Dick was very sad
And cried because his neck was sore,
And not a one said sour things
To anybody any more.

THE BRANCH

We stopped at the branch on the way to the hill.
We stopped at the water a while and played.
We hid our things by the osage tree
And took off our shoes and stockings to wade.

There is sand at the bottom that bites at your feet,
And there is a rock where the waterfall goes.
You can poke your foot in the foamy part
And feel how the water runs over your toes.

The little black spiders that walk on the top
Of the water are hard and stiff and cool.
And I saw some wiggletails going around,
And some slippery minnows that live in the pool.

And where it is smooth there is moss on a stone,
And where it is shallow and almost dry
The rocks are broken and hot in the sun,
And a rough little water goes hurrying by.

THE WORM

Dickie found a broken spade
And said he'd dig himself a well;
And then Charles took a piece of tin,
And I was digging with a shell.

Then Will said he would dig one too.
We shaped them out and made them wide,
And I dug up a piece of clod
That had a little worm inside.

We watched him pucker up himself
And stretch himself to walk away.
He tried to go inside the dirt,
But Dickie made him wait and stay.

His shining skin was soft and wet.
I poked him once to see him squirm.
And then Will said, "I wonder if
He knows that he's a worm."

And then we sat back on our feet
And wondered for a little bit.
And we forgot to dig our wells
A while, and tried to answer it.

And while we tried to find it out,
He puckered in a little wad,
And then he stretched himself again
And went back home inside the clod.

A CHILD ASLEEP

I looked for him everywhere
Because I wanted him to play;
And then I found him on his bed
Asleep, but it was day.

His eyes were shut behind the lids—
He couldn't lift them up to see.
And I looked at him very long,
And something in him looked at me.

And he was something like a cat
That is asleep, or like a dog;
Or like a thing that's in the woods
All day behind a log.

And then I was afraid of it,
Of something that was sleeping there.
I didn't even say his name,
But I came down the stair.

LITTLE BUSH

A Song

A little bush
At the picnic place,
A little bush could talk to me.

I ran away
And hid myself,
And I found a bush that could talk to me,
A smooth little bush said a word to me.

UNCLE MELLS AND THE WITCHES' TREE

He said he was tired and sore all day,
His bones were stiff and his joints were tight.
The witches had turned him into a horse,
And they rode him all that night.

They rode him out by Briartown,
And they stopped by a tree and peeled some switches;
They broke them long and peeled them keen—
Two for each of the witches.

He made the sparks fly out of the stones,
And he swam a creek where there was n't a ford,
Two witches holding onto his back,
And the moon went down in blood. . . .

When we asked him where they let him go,
And what kind of switches they were, said he,
"I would n't dare name that tree," he said,
"I would n't dare name that tree."

AT THE WATER

I liked to go to the branch today;
I liked to play with the wiggletails there.
And five little smells and one big smell
Were going round in the air.

One was the water, a little cold smell,
And one was the mud and that was more,
And one was the smell of cool wet moss,
And one was some fennel up on the shore.

And the one big smell came out of the mint,
And one was something I couldn't tell.
And the five little ones and the big one
All went together very well.

WATER NOISES

When I am playing by myself,
And all the boys are lost around,
Then I can hear the water go;
It makes a little talking sound.

Along the rocks below the tree,
I see it ripple up and wink;
And I can hear it saying on,
"And do you think? And do you think?"

A bug shoots by that snaps and ticks,
And a bird flies up beside the tree
To go into the sky to sing.
I hear it say, "Killdee, killdee!"

Or else a yellow cow comes down
To splash a while and have a drink.
But when she goes I still can hear
The water say, "And do you think?"

AMONG THE RUSHES

I saw a curly leaf and it was caught against the grassy side,
And it was tangled in the watery grasses where the branch is wide;
I had it for my little ark of rushes that must wait and hide.

I had it for my little Moses hidden where no one could see,
The little baby Moses that nobody knew about but me.

And I was hiding in the flags and I was waiting all the day,
And watching on the bank to see if Pharaoh's daughter came that way.

NUMBERS

When I can count the numbers far,
And know all the figures that there are,

Then I'll know everything, and I
Can know about the ground and sky,

And all the little bugs I see,
And I'll count the leaves on the silver-leaf tree,
And all the days that ever can be.

I'll know all the cows and sheep that pass,
And I'll know all the grass,

And all the places far away,
And I'll know everything some day.

THE DARK

There are six little houses up on the hill.

And when it is night,
There are six little windows with light.

The katydids sing and some frogs are about,
And after a while one light goes out,

And then there are five lights still.

The little frogs chirp and I hear a dog bark
Somewhere away in the dark—

Off in the dark far away somewhere
And only four houses are left up there.

And then there are three, and two, and one,
And the one little house with the light goes on

And on, and the dew gets cool,
And just for a moment there comes an owl . . .

Somebody sings three words, just three,
And five cool shivers go over the tree,
And a shiver goes over me.

A night fly comes with powdery wings
That beat on my face—it's a moth that brings

A feel of dust, and then a bright
Quick moment comes to the one little light.

But it flickers out and then it is still,
And nothing is left on the hill.

NUMBER SONG

Sixteen pigeons flew over the spire
Of the church, and as they went higher and higher

They gathered in to be twelve, and ten,
And then they were seven, and then,

When I saw them last they were four—
Wings going and then nothing more.

THE SUN AND A BIRCH TREE

As I came home through Howard's lane,
The trees were bending down with rain.

A still mist went across their tops,
And my coat was powdered gray with drops.

Then I looked in the woods to see
The limbs of the white birch tree.

It made a bright spot in the air,
And I thought the sun was shining there.

IN THE NIGHT

The light was burning very dim,
The little blaze was brown and red,
And I waked just in time to see
A panther going under the bed.

I saw him crowd his body down
To make it fit the little space.
I saw the streaks along his back,
And the bloody bubbles on his face.

Long marks of light came out of my eyes
And went into the lamp—and there
Was Something waiting in the room—
I saw it sitting on a chair.

Its only eye was shining red,
Its face was very long and gray,
Its two bent teeth were sticking out,
And all its jaw was torn away.

Its legs were flat against the chair,
Its arms were hanging like a swing.
It made its eye look into me,
But did not move or say a thing.

I tried to call and tried to scream,
But all my throat was shut and dry.
My little heart was jumping fast,
I couldn't talk or cry.

And when I'd look outside the bed
I'd see the panther going in.
The streaks were moving on his back,
The bubbles on his chin.

I couldn't help it if they came,
I couldn't save myself at all,
And so I only waited there
And turned my face against the wall.

THE GRANDMOTHER

When Grandmother comes to our house,
She sits in the chair and sews away.
She cuts some pieces just alike
And makes a quilt all day.

I watch her bite the little thread,
Or stick the needle in and out,
And then she remembers her grandmother's house,
And what her grandmother told about,

And how a very long ago—
She tells it while she cuts and strips—
We used to live in Mary-land,
And there was a water with ships.

But that was long before her day,
She says, and so I like to stand
Beside her chair, and then I ask,
"Please tell about in Mary-land."

IN MARYLAND

When it was Grandmother Annie's day,
We lived on a hill, and down below,
Beyond the pasture and the trees,
A river used to go.

The water was very wide and blue
And deep, and my! it was a sight
To see the ships go up and down,
And all the sails were white.

And Grandmother Annie used to **wait**
Beside the window or the door.
She never was too tired of it
To watch the river any more.

And we could hardly see across,
And the water was blue, as blue as the sky,

And all day long and all day long
We watched the little ships go by.

THE SUNDAY BONNET

It happened at Grandmother Polly's house,
And there was a bonnet put away
For Polly to wear when she went to church.
She would not wear it every day.

It had some little flowers on,
And it was standing on its head
In a bonnet box where it was safe,
Away up stairs on the company's bed.

And Grandmother Polly was going to church,
And she sent her Alice up the stair—
Alice was black—she was Evaline's child—
She waited on Polly and combed her hair.

And Alice said, "Oh, lawsie me!"
And then she cried and came running down.
And everyone went to see, and the cat
Had five little cats in the bonnet crown.

THE PEOPLE

The ants are walking under the ground,
And the pigeons are flying over the steeple,
And in between are the people.

AUTUMN FIELDS

He said his legs were stiff and sore
For he had gone some twenty-eight miles,
And he'd walked through by water gaps
And fences and gates and stiles.

He said he'd been by Logan's woods,
And up by Walton's branch and Simms,
And there were sticktights on his clothes
And little dusts of seeds and stems.

And then he sat down on the steps,
And he said the miles were on his feet.
For some of that land was tangled brush,
And some was plowed for wheat.

The rabbits were thick where he had been,
And he said he'd found some ripe papaws.
He'd rested under a white oak tree,
And for his dinner he ate red haws.

Then I sat by him on the step
To see the things that he had seen.
And I could smell the shocks and clods,
And the land where he had been.

COLD FEAR

As I came home through Drury's woods,
My face stung in the hard sleet.
The rough ground kept its frozen tracks;
They stumbled my feet.

The trees shook off the blowing frost.
The wind found out my coat was thin.
It tried to tear my clothes away.
And the cold came in.

The ice drops rattled where there was ice.
Each tree pushed back the other ones.
I did not pass a single bird,
Or anything that crawls or runs.

I saw a moth wing that was dry
And thin; it hung against a burr.
A few black leaves turned in a bush;
The grass was like cold, dead fur.

As I climbed over Howard's fence,
The wind came there with a sudden rush.
My teeth made a chattering sound,
And a bush said, "Hush!"

When I was in our house again,
With people there and fire and light,
A thought kept coming back to say,
"It will be cold out there tonight."

The clods are cold and the stones are cold,
The stiff trees shake and the hard air, . . .
And something said again to me,
"It will be cold out there."

And even when I talked myself,
And all the talk made a happy sound,
I kept remembering the wind
And the cold ground.

A LITTLE WIND

A Song

When I lay down
In a clover place,
With eyelids closed,
In a clover place,
A little wind came to my face.

One gentle wind
Blew on my mouth,
And I said, "It will quiver by.
What little wind now can it be?"
And I lay still
Where the clovers were.

But when I raised my lids to see,
Then it was a butterfly.

MR. PENNYBAKER AT CHURCH

He holds his songbook very low,
And then he stretches down his face,
And Mother said, "You mustn't watch,
He's only singing bass."

He makes his voice go walking down,
Or else he hurries twice as fast
As all the rest, but even then
He finishes the song the last.

And when I see him singing there,
I wonder if he knows it all
About Leviticus and Shem
And Deuteronomy and Saul.

THE WOLVES

When Grandmother Polly had married and gone,
But before her father had given her Clem,
Or Joe, or Sandy, or Evaline—
Before he had given her any of *them,*

She used to live in a far-away place,
In a little cabin that was her home,
And all around were bushes and trees,
And the wolves could come.

At night they ran down out of the rocks
And bristled up their trembly fur.
They came and howled by Polly's door
And showed their little white teeth at her.

A BEAUTIFUL LADY

We like to listen to her dress,
It makes a whisper by her feet.
Her little pointed shoes are gray;
She hardly lets them touch the street.

Sometimes she has a crumpled fan.
Her hat is silvered on the crown.
And there are roses by the brim
That nod and tremble up and down.

She comes along the pavement walk,
And in a moment she is gone.
She hardly ever looks at us,
But once she smiled and looked at John.

And so we run to see her pass
And watch her through the fence, and I
Can hear the others whispering,
"Miss Josephine is going by."

SHELLS IN ROCK

I've been along the quarry road,
And I have watched men digging wells,
And everywhere it was the same—
The stones were full of little shells.

And they are packed away in rock;
They're under sand and under clay;
And some one said that they were left
When the ocean went away.

I saw them in the stones that make
A church, and in a bridge.
They're hidden in the solid rock
But they show along the edge.

You see them in foundation stones;
They show in creeks and waterfalls;
And once I saw them on the jail—
More little shells in walls.

We walk on them when we walk on roads;
And they're packed under all the hills.
Suppose the sea should come back here
And gather up its shells.

HORSE

His bridle hung around the post;
The sun and the leaves made spots come down;
I looked close at him through the fence;
The post was drab and he was brown.

His nose was long and hard and still,
And on his lip were specks like chalk.
But once he opened up his eyes,
And he began to talk.

He didn't talk out with his mouth;
He didn't talk with words or noise.
The talk was there along his nose;
It seemed and then it was.

He said the day was hot and slow,
And he said he didn't like the flies;
They made him have to shake his skin,
And they got drowned in his eyes.

He said that drab was just about
The same as brown, but he was not
A post, he said, to hold a fence.
"I'm horse," he said, "that's what!"

And then he shut his eyes again.
As still as they had been before.
He said for me to run along
And not to bother him any more.

THREE DOMINICAN NUNS

One day they came; I heard their feet.
They made a tapping on the street.

And as they passed before our trees,
Their shawls blew out in curves like 3's,
And bent again in 2's and L's;

The wind blew on their rosaries
And made them ring like little bells.

MY HEART

My heart is beating up and down,
Is walking like some heavy feet.
My heart is going every day,
And I can hear it jump and beat.

At night before I go to sleep,
I feel it beating in my head;
I hear it jumping in my neck
And in the pillow on my bed.

And then I make some little words
To go along and say with it—
The men are sailing home from Troy,
And all the lamps are lit.

The men are sailing home from Troy,
And all the lamps are lit.

THE HENS

The night was coming very fast;
It reached the gate as I ran past.

The pigeons had gone to the tower of the church
And all the hens were on their perch,

Up in the barn, and I thought I heard
A piece of a little purring word.

I stopped inside, waiting and staying,
To try to hear what the hens were saying.

They were asking something, that was plain,
Asking it over and over again.

One of them moved and turned around,
Her feathers made a ruffled sound,

IT'S AN OLD
SCOTTISH CUSTOM

NEIL McCALLUM

IT'S AN OLD
SCOTTISH CUSTOM

NEW YORK: THE VANGUARD PRESS, INC.

This book is set in 12 pt. Aldine Bembo, a type-face modelled on the fifteenth-century letter first used by the Venetian printer Aldus Manutius (1450–1515). Aldine Bembo is based on the script of the calligrapher Lodovico degli Arrighi, called Vicentino, and was cut by Francesco Griffo of Bologna.

Aldine Bembo has been revived by the Monotype Corporation from whose matrices it is cast.

PRINTED IN GREAT BRITAIN BY
JARROLD AND SONS LIMITED, NORWICH

CONTENTS

ACKNOWLEDGEMENTS

I have to thank the following authors, owners of copyright, and publishers, for giving permission to include poems and prose passages in this book:

W. H. Murray and J. M. Dent & Sons for the passage from *Undiscovered Scotland*; Sir Alexander Gray for the lines from the poem *Scotland*; Mrs George Bambridge, Methuen & Co., and the Macmillan Company of Canada, for the lines from *McAndrew's Hymn* in Rudyard Kipling's *The Seven Seas*; John Kincaid and the Caledonian Press for the lines from the poem *A Glesca Rhapsodie* in the collection *Fowrsom Reel*; Sorley Maclean and William MacLellan & Co. for the lines of Gaelic poetry from the collection *Dain do Eimhir*; C. M. Grieve (Hugh MacDiarmid) for the poem *The Little White Rose*; John Connell for the passage from *David Go Back*, published by Cassell & Co.

I am indebted to F. Marian McNeill and Blackie & Son for permitting me to dip freely into the gastronomic excellence of *The Scots Kitchen*. I should like to acknowledge the great value of Thomas Davidson's book on witchery and warlockry, *Rowan Tree and Red Thread*, published by Oliver & Boyd, and also Peter F. Anson's *Scots Fisherfolk*, published by the Banffshire Journal for the Saltire Society.

Chapter decorations have been taken from the following volumes: *Ecclesiological Notes on Some of the Islands of Scotland* by T. S. Muir; *Edinburgh Papers* by Robert Chambers; *Scenery of Scotland* by Sir Archibald Geikie; *History of Peeblesshire* by William Chambers; *The Orkneys and Shetland* by J. R. Tudor; *A Tour in Scotland 1772* by Thomas Pennant; *Physiologie du Médecin* by Louis Huart; *Memorials of Edinburgh* by Daniel Wilson; *Scottish Songs Prior to Burns* by Robert Chambers; *The Caledonian Muse* (ed. Joseph Ritson); and *The World of Wit and Humour*.

RUBBING FROM THE MAESHOW TUMULUS, A PREHISTORIC
GRAVE IN THE ORKNEYS

FOREWORD

LIKE GAUL, SCOTLAND IS divided into three parts—the
Highlands, the central industrial belt, and the Lowlands.
They are three quite distinct regions. The Lowlands contain
the best farmland, the central belt contains the best coalfields,
and the Highlands contain the best whisky.

The Highlands are the cynosure. They are a show piece for
tourists who approach them with some incertitude, bearing
in mind stories of the Loch Ness monster, fearing a tartan

9

leg-pull. The Highlands, once they have been seen, leave no sense of deception. It was a young lady who looked at Ben Suilven for the first time and said, with neither approval nor distaste, 'How too, too neolithic'.

There is a history book which describes Scotland as 'a warlike and romantic little country'. As the book was written by a Scotswoman the description must be accepted as a serious valuation. It sums up a regrettably popular attitude. Little countries that are romantic and warlike have been the curse of the world. One cannot love them except when they appear on the stage as the *mise en scène* of Ruritanian light operas. They are a greater nuisance than large countries which, if equally perverse, are more predictable in their follies.

Here one must attempt some kind of definition. Scotland has suffered its burden of romance for too long. It has become insubstantial and nebulous. Is Scotland a country or is it a kind of scenery, or is it something else altogether: a series of ideas and impressions that have accreted, during the course of a great many years, to the hinterland of North Britain?

One recalls another description of Scotland: 'Caledonia stern and wild'. Applied to the countryside this is possibly correct in a general by-and-large way—yet what could be more idyllic and lush than parts of the Merse of Tweed?

There is another Scotland which produces the largest ships in the world, a vast amount of coal, jam and woollen underwear. In the statistics of production, population, method of employment, some definition of Scotland would be achieved and it would contain no reference to rugged warriors and romantic ballads. The country is, of course, defined on the ground: there is a boundary between Scotland and England. At present it is of interest to cartographers and has not even the significance of the Mason and Dixon line.

If one goes further into definitions, one is immediately precipitated into the sternness, the wildness and the romance. These have their place in the emotional attitude to Scotland. How otherwise could the country exercise its fascination for the exile? But patriotism is no explanation because non-Scots, with no natural tie to the country, are astonishingly eager to decorate their family tree with at least one authentic Scottish ancestor.

There are probably as many interpretations of Scotland as there are Scotsmen which is as it should be, because it shows a lively interest in the country. The non-Scot has his own different ideas. He may see the country as the reputed home of tartan, haggis and whisky, which is like understanding the United States in terms of stetsons, clam chowder and soda fountains.

This woolliness and vagueness may be explained by the fact that Scotland is not a political unit. It is in a process of change. It has a specific national past. It may easily become a tartan-decorated province. A number of Scots are disturbed by this downward rush to annihilation. For reasons which to them are quite clear they wish to preserve their country as a national entity. The signing of the covenant for home-rule by two million people, the purloining of the 'stone of destiny' from Westminster Abbey, are straws in the wind. They are also indications of precise desires.

Whether or not these political hopes will mature is outside the province of this book. As much can be said against them as for them, but they cannot be ignored by anyone who enters Scotland even for a week-end. This book is one man's Scotland, and in a few thousand words even that is haphazard, selective and quite inconsequential. It falls between the two stools of modern political realism and traditional romantic myth. Both of these aspects are important. To hint at both but to deal with neither is a device that is itself typically Scottish.

What Scotland does offer, abundantly, is its infinite variety. Scotland is small, beloved and comprehensible. It is also vast in time, and some of its traditions are unbroken from the pre-Christian age. It is contemporary and ancient, and therein is its greatest fascination. The whole human story from primitive man to jet-plane can be sensibly appreciated in an afternoon's stroll. A cigarette lit under a neon sign can be stubbed on a tumulus. That is part of the flavour of Scotland. In the country that developed steam power, wireless telegraphy, modern surgery and radar, there is still, in outlying parts, a Stone Age technique of living, a survival of practices and superstitions which make prehistoric man walk hand in hand with the turbo-jet engineer.

This diversity implies that not only is there a Scotland for every Scot, but another for every visitor. A man may attempt to trace current Gaelic legends to their ancient source; he can examine the Shetland stories of the Nuggle or Shoopiltee which takes the outward form of a pony, with a wheel for a tail, entices a man on to its back and then plunges into a loch to drown him; he can watch the migration of birds a score of miles from his nearest fellow human; he can suffer the packed misery of city slums in their worst European manifestations; he can study 'touching' to cure illness in island communities; he may trace the virile Scottish concept of liberty back to the Middle Ages and see it in relation to the naked men and women who worked in Scottish coal pits last century with iron collars round their necks; he may seek out the Sword Dance of Papa Stour in the far north and relate it to the Sword Actors of Yorkshire, south of the Scottish border; he can study the Scot as philosopher, libertine, engineer and poet; he has his choice of Pictish brochs, Roman camps and Georgian town-planning; he will find that the squalid functionalism of the cities is balanced by the living fairy lore of the sea-girt peninsulas; he can examine a rigid puritanism and discover that all Scots are puritans, or inquire into rural mythologies and be convinced that all Scots are sinful pantheists. He can listen to bagpipes, fish for tasty northern trout, and sail in a small boat past islands of unsurpassed beauty. He will not be bored unless he is caught in the tourist trap of tartan novelties, hotel meals and conducted tours.

These chapters do no more than suggest the diversity of one small country. Their purpose is to entertain. If there are a few paragraphs of serious instruction that is the Scottish way which cannot resist turning a conversation into a sermon: the grave must be taken with the gay. If a few arguments are started and no conclusions reached, that too is a habit of the Scots.

Chapter One

MONS MEG

TO HONOUR ANCIENT TRADITIONS

And there's a hand, my trusty fiere,
And gie's a hand o thine;
And we'll tak a richt guid-willie waught,
For auld lang syne.

THE TRON CHURCH IN Edinburgh stands at the intersection of the High Street and the Bridges. It is built on
the rocky spine of the Old Town of Edinburgh. On one
side is the canyon of the Cowgate and on the other is the
gulf where the Waverley Station lies, sending a perpetual
drift of steamy smoke over the parapet of the North
Bridge.

The Tron is not handsome, but if you gaze long enough there is a delayed effect of grimy steadfastness, a Presbyterian dourness. It is sited a little awkwardly, blocking the traffic, like a silent thrustful man who insists on being noticed.

When a citizen of Edinburgh says to another on the last day of the year, 'Are you going to the Tron to-night?' he is not inquiring about attendance at a religious service. The Tron is the focal point of Edinburgh's New Year celebrations. On the night of Hogmanay, the 31st of December, it is a public rendezvous and thousands gather on the streets outside. Why this should be is a matter for conjecture. The Tron is not old as age is understood in Auld Reekie. It was built quite recently, in 1647, and its most momentous experience was when the steeple collapsed during a great fire that swept away a large part of the High Street in 1824.

The Tron is equipped with four large clocks, one on each side of the steeple. It is probably this convenience that makes it a New Year meeting-place. Farther up the High Street is the Cathedral Church of St Giles, the most important of Edinburgh's historic churches. St Giles has no clock, but it has a chime, a well-known and soft cliché of bells at every quarter. It is unusual for a Presbyterian church to have a chime and this may partly explain why St Giles is regarded by sterner worshippers as regrettably 'high church' in its ritual. The fact remains that the capital's chief church, with its happy crown of Gothic stone, is neglected on Hogmanay. The grimmer Tron, without a chime, is a more fitting background for saturnalia.

It is eleven o'clock on the evening of Hogmanay. The

small beginnings of a crowd gather on the pavements of the Bridges and the High Street. Shops and banks on the corner of the intersection have wisely boarded their windows. The early arrivals have usually reached the limit of their capacity for celebration. The pubs have been closed for an hour and those who cannot fill in the time more purposefully sit in doorways and chuckle over the bottles in their hands and pockets. The police come in strength, admonishing the man who sings too loud, quietening the old lady who cuts an unsteady caper at the road edge, but recognizing that this is a period of privilege. About half-past eleven the crowd is big enough to hold up traffic. Tramcars stop trying to push a way through. Motors are diverted. One no longer sees curious travellers, going to a distant party, gaze out of the windows of their vehicles with an air of patient superiority and unadmitted envy. The Tron is for *hoi polloi*.

There are now thousands in the streets, extraordinarily patient, excited in a subdued way, singing in groups, trying to find room to dance with each other, tilting bottles, working up deliberately and perseveringly to the finale of a brief second. Many are from the slums that lie behind the façades of historic buildings. Uphill and down stretches the gloomy shadow of the High Street at night. The house of the Reformer, John Knox, is a stone's throw away. He was a zealous persecutor of orgies. Round a nearby corner, half-way down a precipitous street, is St Cecilia's Hall, where concert music made its first abortive attempt to return to Edinburgh after the arid years of puritanism. The doors of the Tron are open and a mild glow of light emerges from them. For every thousand outside a handful attends the watch-night service. In most churches there is no service

2

whatsoever. Hogmanay remains with the older gods of saturnalia who began it thousands of years ago.

A bottle crashes to the granite ground. A young woman squeals. A hundred yards up the High Street, where there is no crowd, two policemen are taking a man to the station. The bell of an ambulance trills somewhere out of sight. Someone has collapsed unconscious. Others, hardly more sober, maul him with solicitude and goodwill as they carry him to the safety of a doorway beyond the crowd.

The coming of the New Year is an occasion for hope, for gay optimism, for ambitious dreaming, for cleansing resolutions, for the new leaf that is turned with naïve enthusiasm. A new life is born with the new year. The shortest day is already among the yesterdays. The sun is gaining again in its daily journey above the horizon. Winter will pass. The miracle of spring will happen again. Surely, surely, the New Year will be good and full of blessings.

It is a few minutes to the hour. A current of frenzy moves through the crowd, from person to person, an infectious excitement that mounts till the air is charged with expectation. The singing, the mouth-organs, the dancing, quieten as all eyes fasten on the clock. Time is the thing. The magic moment approaches. Another current, a physical sway, threatens disaster. Hundreds surge under pressure and move like a wedge through their fellows. There are shouts. Ponderous oaths explode like fireworks of emotion. Someone unable to tolerate his seething instincts, has flung a bottle high against the wall of a building. The splinters, and the liquid, descend on those below. The moving wedge of people is cushioned and quietened.

The long minute hand on the Tron touches midnight. A

bell tolls. There is a gasp, a sigh, a shout, a roar. Hats, bottles, gloves, scarves, shoes, fly into the air. The New Year has come. People are kissing, clutching, dancing, fighting, grasping, pulling, shoving, thrusting, drinking, belching, shouting, regurgitating, furiously alive, hectically unconscious. Demos is loose. The mob is king.

Inside the Tron Church a hymn is played on the organ and the music does not pass the barrier of noise at the door.

The tumult dies away. In a few seconds a quietness overcomes the pandemonium, as though a reserve of discipline were exerting itself. The mob breaks up, not noiselessly by any means, but without the explosive abandon of midnight.

There is the sound of bagpipes down the street and an eightsome reel gets going. Two young men stop their erratic wandering at John Knox's House. They sit on the steps.

'Are ye happy?' says one.

'Ay,' says the other and with shut eyes he lifts his smiling face to the sky.

Happy is the same as 'fu' and 'fu' is what it pretends to be, a capacity for the utmost absorption of liquid refreshment. Saturnalia is satiated.

Two people walk away from the hub of the crowd. They stroll along the South Bridge, pause for a moment to look through a railing down to the dark underworld of the Cowgate.

One says to the other reflectively, 'Hogmanay is an experience you can never forget. Not even if you are away for years from Scotland.'

The other answers his mood, in a sing-song voice as

though invoking strange gods. 'It is a pagan festival. As such it has meaning. It belongs to a simpler time when people worshipped the sun and the earth. This time of year is the season of despair translated to relief, when the forces of darkness are vanquished. Hogmanay is the festival of the sun rising again after the shortest day.'

'The strange thing is that Hogmanay *should* be irrelevant in the middle of the twentieth century. Did you look at the people?—thousands of shop assistants and bank clerks, tram drivers and scavengers, with their identity cards and their ration books and their trade union cards, all trying to re-capture a riotous paganism.'

'Quite successfully, too.'

'That is what's so extraordinary. These people—in Edin-burgh or anywhere else—don't belong to a world where the darkness of winter is feared or the sun is worshipped. It might be better if we could all feel that way. But isn't it a little ridiculous to leave picture-houses and dance-halls and stand in the open at midnight and drink to the sun?'

'You're too much of a rationalist. The essential point is that the Scots still suffer from the years of the puritan. Here is a public and recognized occasion on which one can drink a little more than is strictly good for one. If everyone does it no one looks very prominent.'

'Just an excuse for a binge, a blind beano?'

'No, surely not, you must know that. I've put it too crudely. We are always contradicting ourselves, we Scots. There is this reputation for being dour and solitary, whereas nothing is enjoyed more than a great big party. But to-night there *was* something else—you've admitted you felt it. Quite apart from the street lights and the policemen and the paper hats there was, for a few moments, a sense of ritual accomplishment. It *was* Hogmanay, and this *is* the New Year, and the instant of change was felt soberly as a pulse in eternity.'

'Aren't we going to first-foot some friends of yours?'

'Yes. Let's go. There will probably be a glass of Het Pint.'

'Het pint? I don't know it.'

'You'll find the recipe in another chapter.'

Similar scenes, similar conversations, take place all over Scotland. Other countries welcome the New Year, but in Scotland there is an abiding seriousness within the party spirit. Old customs die hard, especially in the small towns and in the country. But even in the cities the 'steamies'—the municipal wash-houses—are fully booked for days ahead. Clothes and linen have to be laundered for the New Year. Housewives throughout the country spend the last days of the old year scouring and polishing. All the rooms are cleaned so that the house may be absolutely spotless at midnight on Hogmanay. Girls, entering the tradition, wash the clothes of their dolls.

Before midnight the ash is removed from underneath the fire. Food and drink are ready for first-footers, the people who carry out the custom of paying calls on their friends in the first hours of the New Year.

It is a peculiar mood that descends on Scotland at Hogmanay, a sense of the temporal in the eternal, a feeling of seriousness that survives the libations of whisky, and sees through the chatter and the kissing and hugging a glimpse of the world spinning in the darkness of the universe.

If one were to introduce the Scottish New Year in the

manner of the B.B.C., striking the common denominator of public approval, the script might be like this:

'It is nearly midnight. A New Year is being born in the tick of a clock. The daylight of the New Year is hurrying westwards, at a thousand miles an hour, across the plains of central Russia. It is black midnight—not pitch black. Stars are shining through patches of cloud that stretch, like a roof with holes in it, across the greater part of Scotland. But in places the night is clear. It is also cold, but without frost, typical weather for the time of year. In the cities the lights shine on thronging populous streets. Everyone has his bottle. A tumultuous acclaim awaits the New Year. The countryside, profoundly quiet, is alive with a thousand noises of birds and beasts. In the stillness of the night Scotland is bounded by noise. Along the heights of the Cheviot hills there is a wind that has a small sharp voice, hissing and whispering, muttering in the grass and the heather and in the cracks of Hadrian's Wall. On the coast the tides move and the waves plunge against the land, each wave running and rushing as though it would mount the shore and penetrate the coast, but always it slackens and withdraws in a sucking undertow and another takes its place to waste its strength on the sand—on the rock—on the cliffs of dark Scotland. A few seconds to go . . . lift your charged glasses. . . . A Happy New Year.'

In such a way, a mixture of solemnity and carousal, the Scotsman greets the first of January.

Chapter Two

TO CLIMB MOUNTAINS

Nievie nievie nick-nack
Which hand will ye tak?
Gin ye're richt or gin ye're wrang
I'll beguile ye if I can.

(A child's rhyme. Both hands are held behind the back:
in one of them is a sweet or some other prize.)

THE MYSTIC IN THE Scot is more profound than the
Kirk elder who is only the embodiment of a piece of
rationalization. Witness the number of schisms and faiths into
which he shatters his belief. It is said that wherever there is a
Macleod there is a Presbyterian church, and wherever there
are six Macleods there are six Presbyterian churches. Something similar might be said of the Scots as a whole. This is
because the Scot is not truly religious. Fundamentally he is a
mystic or an animist. In his uneasy but very serious attempt
to disguise himself as a churchgoer the Scot is continually on

his guard against the upsurge of natural response to natural things. He pretends to see sermons in stones, but it is really the stone he looks at, its shape, its cool roughness, the twinklings of mica, the pleasing colour of a vein of feldspar. For a long time he was brought up to believe that this natural delight was 'wrong' and he succeeded in convincing himself that the sermon only was what he valued.

There is a story that a newly ordained Wee Free minister was once gazing entranced at a splendid sunset when a fellow minister balefully tapped him on the shoulder: 'Have a care lest ye fall into the sin of pantheism!'

But the swaddling clothes of convention cannot hide the elemental nature of the Scot. He responds to the elemental, to the natural, and often to the simple—the unadorned music of peasant songs, the simplicity of a great machine, the delight of a logical argument (hence his proficiency at law and philosophy), the formal structure of Gaelic design, the terse emotion and bald narrative of the Border ballads.

Man is as man is born. The Scot is born with a love of mountains, essentially simple and elemental things. Or, since it is preferable to be precise, the Scot loves mountains because they are his landscape. They attach themselves passionately to the imagination, not only the peaks but the valleys, not only the vertical slopes but the broad upland moors.

In his church the Scot sings devoutly his favourite Psalm 121, 'I to the hills will lift mine eyes'. Behind the sober religious exterior lurks the pagan animist. Meantime his son has reverted to type and spends Sunday climbing the hills.

It is the Highlands that are identified most intimately with the idea of Scotland. It was not always so. There were days before the Scot began to re-discover himself when the mountains were shunned. The romantic revival laid bare the Highlands. Arthur Bryant has written of the Highlands —'the primitive land of mountain and flood made fashionable by Walter Scott's poems and novels'. Before the time of Scott the Highlander himself had left a good account of his mountains in his own language but few people cared to learn Gaelic since it was customary to treat the Gael as a savage whose speech would hardly convey the sentiments of gentlemen. We still lack, for example, an adequate English translation of the eighteenth-century *Praise to Ben Dorain* by Duncan Ban MacIntyre.

Sir Walter Scott began to make the Scots aware of their heritage, The railways did even more by making it possible to explore it. If machines could go north, men might dare to explore the mountain fastnesses. Nowadays wave after wave of people, from the cities and the south, go annually to worship the mountains, to scramble up the easier summits, while the *cognoscenti* of the nailed boots bag their 'Munros'. A Munro is a hill of over 3,000 feet. There are 277 of them.

The Highlands steal the thunder. Their frigid January peaks are the stamping-ground for Himalayan expeditions. In long July days a thousand bivouacs in high corries contain the hardy souls whose passion can only be assuaged against a precipitous wall of gneiss. The Highlands steal the thunder but the whole country is an invitation to those who worship mountains with a less muscular devotion.

The hills of the Borders rise in high lithe curves to a lonely communion with air and sky. In Galloway—'Grey Galloway' as it is unkindly called—the slopes of the Merrick above Loch Enoch lead to country that is wilder than any other part south of the Highland line. Here is desolation that teaches the senses a new regard for those fearful remnants of superstition which, from the security of an arm-chair, are tossed away as old wives' tales. There is more of this foreboding atmosphere in Galloway, between Loch Enoch and Loch Neldricken and in the mountains of the Rhinns of Kells, than anywhere else.

In the far north are the fantastic mountains, the aboriginal monoliths of Canisp, Suilven and the smaller Stac Polly. They have been climbed, but I cannot say why. It is enough to look at them, rising in the sheer rock-naked glory of antiquity, sculptured towers of Torridon sandstone that are far beyond the emotional overtones of landscape adjectives. 'Grand', 'magnificent', 'terrible', have no meaning. Those mountains defy the romantic revival and its descriptive stock-in-trade. They are the oldest mountains in Europe—I do not know about the rest of the world.

The Cairngorms, which Queen Victoria found so 'pretty', were once a plateau which has been eroded leaving a number of peaks of the same height, the level of the old plateau. In the north-west this process of erosion and denudation has been going on much longer. Canisp and Suilven are old, as one measures the age of hills. Part of the original creation of hills, they have become the last perpendicular survivals of a vanished continent. They are like a couple of stubborn teeth found in the emptiness of an ancient burial cell.

The hard spine of mountainous Scotland is made by the mountains of the West Highlands, south of Suilven and Canisp: the Slioch, the mountains above Glen Affric, the

Cuillin in Skye, Ben Nevis in the Lochaber group, the intricate pattern of mountains and sea-lochs down to Ben More in Mull, the mountains of Badenoch, the western Grampians, Argyll. It is to the west that people go if they take their mountains, like their whisky, with a little water. The islands, the sea-lochs and the mountains are a happy combination. The intensity and purity of the greens and the blues is not British. There are no pastel shades: it is a land for the oil-painter not the water-colourist. It is Grecian—and there we have it, the comparison has to come. It has been made before, but apologetically, as though the occasion were rare. It is not rare; it is one of the natural and frequent presentations of the west Highlands. (The converse is true, also: I remember flying above the Gulf of Corinth and peering over the wing at mist-shrouded rain-obscured Mount Parnassus: 'How like Scotland,' I thought.)

The Cuillin ridge has a fabulous attraction. People go there, or as near as they can in comfort, to make a pilgrimage. The half-circle of savage hills, most of them 'Munros', is a Mecca for the mountain worshipper. The half-circle contains Loch Coruisk, most easily approached by sea and which, as William Sansom has written, is 'reputed to be the most desolate and terrifying place in the British Isles'.

I went there once with a companion. We travelled on foot from Sligachan along the east of the mountains and then by a comparatively low part of the encircling ridge to

> *that dread shore,*
> *That sees grim Coolin rise and hears Corrisken roar.*

This was the heart of the wilderness of romantic desolation.

It was warm and calm. There had been days of sunshine and from Portree the Cuillins had looked like a few old crones huddled over a cup of tea. Nearer at hand they looked like rugged but benevolent old men. There were butterflies on the wild flowers and a pleasantly pastoral air like a Swiss valley. We had come prepared to spend the night in the open. Above Loch Coruisk there was a small river that reached into the interior of the half-circle of mountains. We walked there in the evening. The valley sides grew steep and the sinking sun threw a deep shadow and this shadow moved up the sides of the opposite mountains, making the valley sink into the earth.

A wind came from the mountains and pressed the heather and the grass like a huge hand. It took the surface of Coruisk and beat it into waves. A mist followed, falling down the bastions of rock from the upper air like water poured from a roof, dropping in heavy skeins. It rained. We crept under boulders and climbed into our sleeping-bags.

At half-past three in the morning sleep was ended. The valley filled with the noise of wind. A gale was leaping across the peaks three thousand feet overhead. It used the basalt columns and precipices like the pipes of an unearthly organ. The black furious titanic wind sent its shrieks of demoniac mirth down to the sounding-board of the valley.

Six feet from where we lay there was a waterfall. There had not been a trickle a few hours before. By four o'clock, in a haggard dawn, we were on our way, sodden and chilled. The most direct route out of the valley was straight ahead, by way of the mountains. At two thousand feet we climbed out of the rain. Five hundred feet later it began to rain again but soon the weather cleared. Below, in the abyss from which we had climbed, hundreds of streams were spilling into the depths. They were white as milk. In rivulets, in torrents, in cascades, in frivolous patterns of lace, the white water gushed from the mountains as though the rock had been punctured. As we watched, clouds began to form. They lifted upwards, twining like shrivelled fingers till they met tendrils of mist on the mountain-tops and then blew away on the wind. Sgurr nan Gillean, Brauch na Frithe, Sgurr na Banachdich, Sgurr Dearg, and Sgurr Alasdair, took off their night-caps. When we had climbed for three hours we crossed the watershed on a saddle between two peaks. Loch Coruisk, glistening in the new sun, was no broader than the span of a hand.

Though we had not asked for the triumphs of a mountaineer they were bestowed on us, not only the awe and the natural wonder at the Cuillin peaks, but the more human delight of being alone on the heights of a mountain, with the world abasing itself at our feet and, beyond the rim of the hills, a distant, unseen land of flat shires and towns populated by pedestrian dullards and sluggish valley-dwellers.

The hills and the winds that scour them come into Scottish literature again and again, with the implication that in a perishable world these things endure and a man fastens to them his thoughts of eternity. 'Corrie and mountain are the natural altars of the earth, to be used as such before we go.' This was said of his own Scottish mountains by the Himalaya climber, W. H. Murray, whose writing on mountaineering catches the ineffable spirit of high places. Describing a winter climb of An Teallach (The Forge), a six-peaked mountain in Wester Ross, he writes of the view from the fourth tower of the fourth peak:

From this last viewpoint the knife-edged dyke behind us looked extraordinarily sensational, nicked along its crest by our footsteps. The whole mountain-scene around—plum-coloured isles and bays, bared teeth of the Cuillin fifty miles south-west, the clean dazzle of the Highland ranges—this whole, rich panorama fell into place as a mere backcloth to the drama of An Teallach's crest. Towers and edges hung in space without visible means of support, hung over the frozen void of the east corrie, but turned to the sunny south a gay lining of snow. The edge ran stark between; it alone seemed fully real, and really true, the essential An Teallach which bore us.

It is the mountains, remote, unpeopled, arrogant in isolation, that are worshipped. The lower hill country is honoured because it supports the peasant hardiness of the Scots. In his poem *Scotland* Sir Alexander Gray writes of the communion between the Scots and those massive hills that cut the sky like whale-backs, that lift their smooth summits over two thousand feet in unprecipitous curves, and are called 'uplands':

> *This is my country*
> *The land that begat me.*
> *These windy spaces*
> *Are surely my own.*
> *And those who here toil*
> *In the sweat of their faces*
> *Are flesh of my flesh,*
> *And bone of my bone.*

Chapter Three

TO BE LEAL TO THE BORDERS

Leal—true-hearted, faithful. Land o' the Leal, the home
of the blessed after death—Paradise, not Scotland.
(*Chambers's Dictionary*)

WAT ARMSTRONG HAS GREEN fingers. He looks after
the flowers and vegetables in a walled garden in the
Borders. Below his cottage is a small river thickly populated
with trout and grayling. Wat is no fisher but his brother-in-
law comes from town to wage war on the fish, sometimes
with a legitimate rod but often with a noose of fine gauge
brass wire which gives excellent sport and allows him to

select his fish with the deliberation of a tourist choosing his lunch in the fish-tank of a Swiss hotel.

The garden is in a bowl of land above the stream. On the pink sun-stroked wall the apple and plum trees are perfectly trained. They lie against the curving wall, and their growth has been guided into so regular a pattern of trunks and branches that they have become formal decorative patterns. The door to the terraced lawns is of iron-studded timber, older than the garden and the fruit trees.

'Over a hundred years ago they were rebuilding part of the house—that's when they put on the turrets—and they laid out the garden and put in this door. It came from the house and it was right old then.'

In the potting-shed, between the lower end of the garden and the river, Armstrong watches the rain when it keeps him away from the bean rows and the tattie beds and he becomes philosophic about the contemporary blooms and the ancient valley in which they grow.

'Armstrongs and Elliots, ride thieves all,' goes the old tag. Armstrong knows it. 'I've settled down. It's more comfortable.'

The rebuilt house is now an hotel. The comical nineteenth-century turrets hold either baggage or wash-basins. But the ground floor has not been titivated with mock Gothic. The walls are four feet thick on the kitchen level and are fifteenth-century at the latest.

'It's not the age,' says Armstrong. 'Godsakes, there's nothing in age but rheumatics and green mould for old bones or old stones. But you feel alive here. It's something mental it does to you—living beside things that have been here for years. It's the next best thing to what they call economic security.' He nods his head, a minimum of gesture which outside the Lowlands would have required a sweep of the hand to indicate the full depth of meaning.

His fingers knead a box of leaf-mould. 'This weather always minds me of the old ballads. They're full of wet and bad weather. To-day the rain's falling like it would never stop the way it must have seemed those days that war and murder would never stop. And when their lads were killed what songs they made of it:

> With ae link o' his yellow hair,
> I'll bind my heart for evermair.

And think of that man stark dead behind a turf dyke:

> In ahint yon auld fail dyke,
> I wot there lies a new-slain knight,
> And naebody kens that he lies there,
> But his hawk and his hound and his lady fair.

There's a bit too much chivalry in that—too aristocratic— but you can see it right enough. God, it would be weather like this with the rain washing the blood into the turf.'

The garden is of two acres, a sun-trap, when there is a sun, and sunk below the lawn and guarded by trees so that the wind that blows the rooks from the tree-tops to the turrets is hardly felt. But the growth can be felt, the Kerr's Pinks swell wonderfully and in the greenhouse, where the artificial heating apparatus is broken, the peaches and the grapes bend the training wires.

Up the valley, two miles hard going along a road that becomes a path and then a foot-track, the land lifts to the surrounding foothills. On an isolated hillock there is a group of trees growing in a circle about fifty yards in diameter.

They grow out of a high circular wall of earth and stone that was a hill-fort in the dark ages. The rampart is covered with grass and is still high enough to prevent a man seeing over. There are four gaps in the wall, gateways at each quarter of the defences. A couple of generations ago someone began to dig into the wall for the materials it contained, probably to use the stones for building. A local man of authority, with a passing interest in history, put a stop to this and tried to prevent further damage by planting the trees. The trees have become so huge that their roots are doing more damage than the dead man with his spade.

There is both isolation and protection within the circle of trees. The succulent valley, with its peaches and its trout, is only two miles away to the north, but it is part of another world. To the south, over the bare land where the thin grass moves in the wind, are the Cheviots where the ground rises into the sky in an escarpment of smooth curves over which the rain comes with the south-west wind. The Cheviots have the appearance of a barrier, a ponderous finite termination of a territory. They contain the Debatable Land, a bone of contention between Scotland and England, a no-man's-land of pillage and murder and the heroism of necessity. The Border line was settled finally last century, and only then because it was necessary to put it on a map.

Somewhere to the east, a few miles across small hills of steep sides and curved tops, is the high road to England, rising up the Jed valley to Carter Bar.

There is a traditional approach to some countries, a route of convenient entry that has become a convention. The Statue of Liberty, as it is called, marks the gateway to the

States. The white cliffs of Dover lead to England. With Scotland things are different. Not an entry but an exit has been hallowed by time and Doctor Johnson. 'The Scotsman's noblest prospect is the high road to England.'

The niff-naffish patriotism of Boswell, who altered his feelings to suit his company, may have irritated Johnson into the phrase that has become something of a proverb. Taken literally there is a good deal of truth in it. There are two low roads, by Berwick and by Gretna, but the high road by Carter Bar is the noblest.

Face north at the top and the view is magnificent. Numerous hills and a complexity of small valleys (including that where Armstrong has his garden) lead to the broad Merse of Tweed. Beyond that are other hill ranges, repeating in the distance until the horizon is reached in dove-grey northern mistiness. The view can be translated, item by topographical item, into a gazetteer of history and legend, fact and fancy, the soul of a nation, the text-book of a sociologist, the paradise of a landscape painter. This may have been what the old bear meant, if the matter is important at all, when he delivered himself of his oracle. But one doubts it, for Johnson was a city man, with dull city values in many things.

From its source in the roots of bog-myrtle and heather, past the uplands where wild turkeys roost in the tree-tops at Dawyck, to the great pastures and parklands of the estuary, the river Tweed travels ninety-seven miles, a small essay in the diversity of land that can be labelled 'Temperate Europe'.

The valley divides into three, the wild upper reaches of Tweedsmuir and Talla, heather and sheep, yellow tormentil growing in mist; the middle reach where the small towns gather, Peebles, Innerleithen, Walkerburn, Melrose, where life is mostly rural, slightly industrial in a clean unobtrusive way, and very individual. From Kelso to the sea the Tweed landscape becomes southern, a pattern of woods and rides and fertile farms where herds of cows are knee-deep in grass. There is a nursery-story air of unreal perfection. Great trees of splendid foliage line the banks of the river. Swans float on the smooth surface. There is a hint of the Lady of Shalott and the music of Sibelius, un-English overtones in this un-Scottish part of the Borders, where the boundary between the countries crosses the Tweed some miles above Berwick and the river passes its last miles in the southern country.

The River Till, a deep turgid waterway of sullen charm, enters Tweed near the field of Flodden. The Till is honestly romantic, in a foreboding Arthurian way. It lingers on its curves with a luxurious weariness.

> Tweed said to Till
> 'What gars ye rin so still?'
> Said Till to Tweed,
> 'Though ye rin wi' speed,
> An I rin slaw,
> For ae man ye droon
> I droon twa.'

On the Till, a mile or so from the Tweed, is the English village of Etol which might have been transported from Buckinghamshire. Its thatched houses stand in two rows under immemorial elms; the inn is a convivial hostelry which opens on Sundays with no puritanical fuss.

It is the middle stretch of Tweed, from Broughton to Kelso, that is the essential Border country. The landscapes have their own palpable personality, shot with continual reminders of the valley's austere origins, and foretastes of the river's final lush miles.

The great tributaries of Yarrow, Ettrick and Teviot, the waters of the Rule and the Jed, come northwards to the Tweed across the uplands that reach to the Cheviots. The broad land they traverse is the deep rural centre of the Borders. It again is as varied as the Tweed valley itself, but there is a different motif. Whereas the river has length, comes from one place and goes to another, this southern tract has breadth, an expansiveness of air and light and colour, but of generous extremes that include glasshouse peaches, isolated farmsteads where shepherds cover twenty miles in a day without seeing another person, small market towns with ruined cathedrals, woollen underwear factories and Roman forts.

This is the oldest region of Scotland, not geographically but in the manner of life. Between the Tweed and the Cheviots there has been less intrusion, less upheaval in historic times, less of industry's revolution, less movement of peoples, than anywhere else in the country. These things are traceable not only in the settled manner of living, but in vocabulary, speech rhythms, in pronunciation. The dialect of the southern Borders is nearest to the Anglian speech, the Teutonic tongue of the people who supplanted the Celts.

The Borders are Lowland. Gaeldom has no meaning here. The most tangible links between the Borders and the Highlands are such historic symbols as Sir Walter Scott's great-grandfather's beard which was 'unblemished by razor or scissors, in token of his regret for the banished dynasty of Stewart'.

In the country playgrounds children still chant their counting runes: eenity, feenity, fickity, fegg, ell, bell, domin's egg, irky, birky, starry rock, an, tan, too's Jock. And some of them walk to school along roads that are unmetalled and have existed since the Romans made them.

This land was the limit of the Roman empire. It was occupied, rather tentatively at times, by garrison forces who came with both peace and a sword. There is no record of great battles. (These took place farther north where, as one man put it, 'the Roman backsides were skelped and the Roman noses were turned towards Rome'.) In the Borders the Romans were sternly patriarchal. They destroyed the hill-top forts of the Celts and tried to teach the discipline of Latin civilization, creating new villages and turning the inhabitants into imperial workers, servants and batmen. They had less success than they hoped, for the northern Celts kept them occupied, but they went as far as sharing their gods with the local deities and left a Roman altar to the Celtic triple-mother goddess.

Much nearer the present time are the ballads and they, more than any of the later literature that has dealt with the Borders, are a mirror of the people. This may be what attracts men like Wat Armstrong. The ballads are written in his own language and concern his own ancestors. In the Borders roots go deep. There is a feeling that the present day is the present chapter of a continuous story. It is unusual to find this sense of historic continuity so deeply developed. It is more than village patriotism, though a man is a Borderer, a Scot, and a Briton, in that descending order. The purposeful emotion and vitality of a Border common-riding is far more than would be merited by a symbolic pageant. There is a sense of 'belonging', of being part of a movement through time that has significance. The danger is that this feeling for the history of things can lead through romanticism to sentimentality.

Scott's remarkable edifice, Abbotsford, stands in its grounds beside the Tweed, not only as a monument to a man's genius, but as a memorial to exaggeration. Scott, who did so much to revive an interest in the past, and who is suffering now from the reaction to romanticism, was unable to write about the realities of his own time. It was not the Borders, or Scotland, that he described, but that twice-removed other world that a critic has called 'Scott-land'.

(There is a footnote to Scottiana that is worth making. In Ashiesteel, the Tweedside home that Scott inhabited before he built Abbotsford, there is a bath that he used. It is built of stone-work, in the manner of its day, on the floor of a small room in the kitchen premises. In later years, when more luxurious plumbing had been installed, the bath that once contained the Wizard's ablutions, saw service as a coal-store. It makes an interesting addition to social records of 'coals in the bath' behaviour.)

Wat, in his potting-shed, is wondering if the weather will be fair for the village flower and vegetable show on the Saturday. There is a dance afterwards. His wife is making fadge, a bannock that is oven-baked. She hopes it will win a prize at the show. His elder boy is making a collection of wild fruits and berries to show in the children's section. He and his wife will cycle home from the dance and on the following Sunday, if the weather is good, he will attend the annual open-air memorial service for the Battle of Otterburn, an event of the year 1388.

So it's a fine idyllic life he leads, his fingers grubbing the good earth, with a Saturday dance and a drink at the Horse and Hound, and now and then a commemoration service or a common-riding for the sake of history, and a dip in the ballads showing a taste for literature. It's right fine, what with fifty families in the small valley living in condemned cottages and not a sign of new houses being built while the rain comes up inside the walls because there is no damp course and the landlord doesn't forget to collect the rent.

And there is a long walk through all weathers for the children every day they go to school because it's off the bus route and there is an argument with a department at St Andrew's House, Edinburgh, about whether or not the department is liable within the interpretation of the Act governing the situation for the provision of transport at public expense. 'Damn the argument,' says Wat, 'it's been going on for years now. My father walked the same road, but he didn't have any shoes, so maybe there's something to be said for progress.'

Chapter Four

TO RIDE THE COMMON

It's fye upon yellow and yellow,
An' fye upon yellow and green,
But up wi' the true blue an' scarlet,
An' up wi' the single sol'd shoon,
It's up wi' the Souters o' Selkirk,
For they are baith trusty an' leal,
An' up wi' the men o' the Forest,
An' doon wi' the Merse to the deil.

T HE LITTLE TOWNS OF the Borders are Peebles,
Galashiels, Melrose, Hawick, Selkirk, Jedburgh, Kelso,
Lauder, Innerleithen, Walkerburn, Stow, Earlston, Duns
and, on the far side of the Tweed watershed, Langholm.

There are no cities. In the Middle Ages there was a town of Roxburgh, the seat of Scottish kings, but it has vanished and not a stone remains. Only the name survives in the county of Roxburghshire.

Many of the oldest towns are royal burghs. Some possess abbeys which are in ruins from warfare and the vandalism of the religious reformers. There is also an abbey at Dryburgh, where there never was a town. The ruined abbeys have a solid, almost monstrous beauty and shattered dignity. They are the weathered relics of an age that has passed completely. No fat friars look after the gardens at Gattonside. The holy processions that moved from Jedburgh to Kelso, to Dryburgh and Melrose, would to-day be as foreign as almond blossom in this land of weavers and shepherds, trout fishers and Rugby football players.

But the ruins remain, part of the enduring atmosphere of the Border country, where the skyline of smooth hills is itself part of the timelessness. The Border abbeys are more massive than the abbeys of southern England. The English spires soar above the flat land, tapering columns of Gothic stone pointing to heaven, but the Border abbeys sit solidly in the good land of the valleys, not attempting to compete with the hills in reaching skywards. (The hills were a refuge: it was to them and not to the cellars that the Covenanters went when they were forbidden to preach in church.)

The land around the Border towns is partly the rich valley country of the Merse of Tweed, but it is the hills and the high moors that give the Borders their lean vitality. The windy uplands are the cradle of the thrawn weather-beaten farmers and shepherd, the hardy stock from which most Scots are descended. 'Is he lonely, you ask?' said a man of a

Border shepherd who rarely leaves his hills. 'Lonely! Na, na, he has the hills and the sky and his work, what more could a man ask! And if he wants a little intelligent conversation he just has a talk with himself!'

A persistent suggestion that the Borders were made by special creation is one of the charms of the region. In the wilder valleys of Ettrick and Yarrow, in the desolate moorland and the high hills, it is permissible to wonder if the process of creation is yet finished.

In the towns there is a spirited rivalry so that a Selkirk man considers himself worthier than a Gala man, who thinks he is better than a Hawick man, who believes he has no superior at all. Throughout the year all these towns put their traditions on display, and each in its own way commemorates incidents in its history and carries out ancient customs.

The Selkirk celebrations develop the theme of the battle of Flodden in 1513, but undoubtedly some of the observances go farther back than that. At Jedburgh, where the game of hand-ba' is played in the streets, it is said that the ball is the symbolic head of the English garrison commander of Ferniehirst castle, a few miles up the valley. But hand-ba' is older than the wars with England and was once played throughout the Lowlands.

The men of Selkirk go once a year to the small village of Lilliesleaf to play bowls in the streets. At Hawick they sing 'Teribus and Teri Odin, sons of heroes slain at Flodden', and then explain that Flodden is quite a recent event in the town's history because the song goes back to Thor and Odin. There is a mound of land that has always been known as Hawick Moat. A visitor asked a native the origin of this. 'Can you tell me if it is artificial or natural?' The Hawick man put on a look of outraged patriotism: 'It's neither, it's Hawick Moat.'

Half a dozen of the towns concentrate their particular ceremonies into a few days of furious ritual and merriment. Those are the days of the Border common-ridings, none of which clashes with another so that a person may move from one town to the next during the summer months. The essential qualifications to take full part in the common-ridings are a good seat on a horse and a good liver.

The common-ridings are basically similar in purpose, though details vary. Curds and cream are ceremoniously eaten, whisky is ceremoniously drunk, turf and stones, symbols of proprietorship, ceremoniously change hands. Each town is laying claim to the ownership of its common land. Those lands were acquired in the past either by gift or purchase. A king, recognizing a service, made a gift of land, or the ground may have been held tenaciously by the town against the ambitions of a baron equipped with the power of 'the pit and the gallows'. The annual common-riding maintained the town's ownership valid in law.

The hospitable town of Lauder, a Royal and Ancient Burgh of less than seven hundred inhabitants, has a celebration when the main street is packed with bandsmen and horses and cheering children. The boundary riders go far into the hills—for many of the towns possess extensive lands —and half-way round their course they gather in a field with nothing in view but dry-stane dykes and a small wood. The bare hills slope under the arch of the sky and the curlews and peewits cry above the neighing and stamping of the horses. There is a bite to eat and a stirrup-cup of the 'auld kirk'—a nickname for whisky. The provost and the town band have come by road. A few words are said, a few songs are sung, and then the riders gallop off to continue the round of the boundary and the others return to town to welcome them back. Everyone then adjourns to the handsome and unusual town hall where libations of the burgh whisky are handed round in ample glasses. The man who jogs your elbow may be a belted earl, against whose ancestral avarice the common-riding was directed, or he may be a professional poacher who has come for the day from Peebles, or anyone at all, or no one. The excellent and copious burgh whisky is a most effective layer of social distinction, more effective even than the general but drouthy tradition that 'we're a' Jock Tamson's bairns'.

At Hawick it was once the custom for small boys to be beaten at various landmarks on the boundary. This was not to punish them but to ensure that they did not forget the extent of the town's property. The oldest common-ridings are those at Hawick, Selkirk and Lauder. In other towns the custom has either been interrupted and recently revived or it is a new piece of picturesque pageantry grafted to other customs. But at Hawick, Selkirk and Lauder the common-riding has taken place for centuries, and it is in those towns that the sense of antiquity is strongest.

At Selkirk the celebrations start in May when the standard-bearer is chosen. He is a young man. He must have been born in Selkirk, be single, and have ridden the marches regularly. There is a concert to mark his election. Traditional songs are sung by a huge audience: *O' a' the Airts; Up wi' the Souters; The Flowers o' the Forest*. It is an occasion of great sentiment and emotion.

The Souters, as the Selkirk people call themselves, are aware of their history. A speech is given at the concert, usually by an 'exile' invited home for the occasion. He draws a picture of Selkirk down the centuries. The audience sits enraptured. This is their town, and they are its living inheritors. Their country's laws were once passed in the old castle that has vanished. Medieval guilds maintained authority and prosperity in spite of the numbers who had to go to 'the wars'. The speaker tells of the battle of Flodden and how one of the few survivors came back with the news of the defeat that turned Selkirk into a town of mourning. There are tears in the eyes of the audience as they hear of this tragedy of over four hundred years ago. The town is easing its civic emotions for the greater day that lies a month ahead.

The day before the common-riding is known as the 'nicht afore the morn'. In the evening there is the public 'crying of the burley' when a town official, in dark uniform and top hat, announces to the sound of fife and drum that the boundaries of the burgh will be ridden next day. The town is gay with flags. In the market square carpenters are erecting the wooden platform where the colours will be 'cast' after the boundaries have been ridden.

There are a great many parties. The pubs are full. In the streets men and women suddenly burst into one of the traditional songs. This itself is a strange thing because the Lowland Scots are by nature reserved and cautious and in the ordinary way would as soon think of singing in the streets as having a bath in public.

Buses and cars arrive filled with passengers, mostly 'exiles' from Edinburgh and other parts of Scotland, from London, and every year there are some from other parts of the world, their visit to the homeland timed to coincide with the common-riding of their home town. The social gaiety is infectious. Strangers talk to strangers. 'Man, it's twenty years since I was here, and this year I said, come what may, I'll be at the common-riding. I flew last week from New-foundland.' 'I missed it last year and the year before because the bairns were ill both times. It's not so far I've got to come, about twenty miles, but I couldn't leave the bairns. This year they're with me.'

They come in their hundreds and thousands until Selkirk is packed from the Toll Bridge to the Back Raw. There is hospitality, and songs, and meetings, and stories and reminiscences, and everyone's a Souter and proud of it, and everyone's everyone's friend and there are drinks all round and young men and women move up and down the streets linked arm in arm in lines that reach from one row of houses to the next.

On the outskirts of the town is another invasion. Into the fields and paddocks and stables come horses and ponies, hacks and hunters, ancient nags, and thoroughbreds that will ride the marches and then take part in a gymkhana.

'The nicht afore the morn' is a party, with decorum behind the enthusiasm. Behind the parties and the meetings and the songs is the sincere pride in being Souters. People are refresh-ing themselves with their legends as well as with 'barley bree'. The sense of history, of having roots in an important community, is genuine and it is this that makes the common-ridings an astonishing revelation to the stranger. It is not a mock-up of pageantry, nor a deliberate effort to swell with pompous pride, as happens when a nation puts on a Great

Exhibition. In Selkirk (as in Hawick and Lauder) the spirit behind the common-riding is as authentic as the cobbles in the streets or the seasons of the year.

Next day there is an early start. At seven in the morning the riders set off. They have to cover about fourteen miles of hill and valley in two hours. The band plays, final whiskies are swallowed (though the hip-flasks are full) and eight hundred hooves clatter through the town and 'ower the green'. In front, carrying the honoured burgh flag, a replica of the colours brought back from Flodden, is the standard-bearer, drawing the shrill cheers of children and the huzzahs of the watching crowd. Thousands of voices cry 'Safe oot, safe in'.

About nine o'clock those who are horseless gather at the Toll Bridge and on a small hill provided with crush-barriers they wait for the riders to return. On a high ridge more than a mile away a horse appears, first of the two hundred on the way back from the Three Brethren, a young mountain that lies between the rivers Yarrow and Tweed and is the summit of the ride. Someone picks out the flying colours of the standard-bearer. Slowly the riders gather together and with the standard-bearer at the head they move towards the road and the town like an invading band of skirmishers. They come down the hill like the solid cavalry of an army.

When the riders are back, a huge noisy procession of horses and brass bands, pipes and drums and pedestrians, slowly moves to the town square where the standard-bearer 'casts' his colours and is followed by other bearers of flags representing the craft guilds and many different associations. Each goes separately to the wooden dais. This is the last and most solemn part of the common-riding. A band plays softly as the heavy flags swing and sway in the air. Even the horses are quiet so that the ripple of the flags is audible above the notes of the music.

There are new wreaths on the memorial to those who lost their lives at Flodden. The rest of the day is a holiday.

Chapter Five

TO LIVE ON ISLANDS

> To the southern inhabitants of Scotland the state of
> the mountains and the islands is equally unknown
> with that of Borneo or Sumatra.—Dr Johnson.

NOWADAYS THE CRY IS for the south, for the sun, and
the Drang nach Süden may be an army of soldiers or
a bus-load of twittering tourists. The ancients looked to the
north. Scotland was a rampart of mountains and beyond it
were the islands in the seas of the north. Ptolemy drew
Scotland running lengthwise from west to east and Ultima
Thule must have been somewhere beyond the West Highland sandstone and gneiss.

Islands preserve a way of life. They are less open to what
used to be called progress but is now more abstractly described as 'influences'. The sea protects and defends, and the
Atlantic waves still preserve songs and language that have
vanished from most of the mainland. Centres of civilization

in the past have found their main strength on the islands. The 'small dark men' of legend retreated to the safer foam-surrounded bastions and no doubt prospered, as the Orcadians prosper to-day. St Donnon used the islands as stepping-stones for the propagation of the gospel and marked his progress with the building of cells and churches which to-day give their ruined testimony to a vigour that has passed. When the Norsemen came, about the eighth century, they made themselves masters of a kingdom of islands and for four centuries they ruled the Shetlands, the Orkneys, the Hebrides, parts of the mainland, and groups of islands down the west coast of Scotland and England to St George's Channel.

The Norse influence was considerable. The men came without women and married Celtic wives. There was a complete intermingling of the two peoples. The conquest remains in speech and customs and, oddly enough, in the title of a bishop of the Church of England. The bishop whose seat is on the Isle of Man is known as the Bishop of Sodor and Man. Sodor is all that is left of the Sodorn Islands, the name the Norse gave the Hebrides (Sudreyjar—Southern islands). The bishop has long ceased to have a pastoral interest in Scottish islands.

Beyond the ragged seismographic edge of the north-west seaboard is fabulous Skye. Beyond it, in the deeper seas, is the rampart of the Hebrides, itself fabulously washed by the Gulf Stream so that a man, with a little care, may grow a palm tree in the open if he does not mind it being bent like a bow by the Atlantic winds. A few other islands fall roughly into place in a mental map of this unmemorizable region. South of Skye are the islands whose names chime with the echoes of a school-room lesson—Tiree, Coll, Muck, Eigg,

Rum, Canna. These islands remain in the mind, in strict sequence, like the declension of *mensa*.

There are others with the sound of the sea in their syllables —Gometra, Treshnish, Iona, Lunga, Lismore, Kerrara. Colonsay and Oronsay are rhyming twins off Jura whose paps lie against the night sky like the breasts of a supine monolithic goddess.

The east coast offers little, but what there is has been seized on by history and legend—the Isle of May, the notorious Bell Rock, and the quadruplets in the Firth of Forth, sounding like a firm of lawyers—Inchcolm, Inchkeith, Inchmickery and Bass. Robert Louis Stevenson put David Balfour on the Bass, and many others have been put there in past centuries for less romantic reasons.

The mouth of the Clyde estuary is stoppered by the Cumbraes, Big and Little. The latter is a few miles in length and somewhat less in width. It was here that a minister used to pray to the Almighty to extend His protection from the Cumbraes to the adjacent islands of Great Britain and Ireland. To the south-west is Arran where one can prospect for gold in Glen Sannox and where the Gaelic language is on the very precipice of extinction. About half a hundred old people still know it. They are all over sixty-five.

There are other islands one might wrench from a reluctant memory, but they are few compared with the possible total. The Summer Isles, the Isles of the Sea, Foula, St Kilda . . . the list is not unending but it is as long as an old-fashioned sermon. There are seven hundred islands around Scotland, and two hundred of them are inhabited.

The northernmost Scottish island is Unst in the Shetland group. I lived there once, on the hill of Saxa Vord, in a hut nine hundred feet above the sea. Out in the ocean, on the isolated rock of Muckle Flugga, were three lighthouse keepers. They had the strange honour, *ex officio*, of being the northernmost inhabitants of the British Isles. On my desolate hill-top, I had fourth place in this comparison of latitudes.

A pair of great skuas, or bonxies, nested near me. They are fierce birds and breed only on Shetland and St Kilda. To protect their young they have a technique of diving from a height and striking at a human head with their feet.

To reach Saxa Vord there had been a piece of complicated travel by train to Inverness, by air to the south of Shetland, and then by a succession of vehicles and motor boats moving northwards into more desolate and beautiful country. There was green water, islands of many colours, sea-birds unfolding bright wings against the sky, and seals moving their distressingly human bodies over the rocks. Above all, greater than the brilliance of colour, was the sense of space, of being in sensory contact with leagues of air and water, the two absolutes of the north.

The island of Yell was a stepping-stone between the mainland of Shetland and Unst. Its place-names were Norse—Ulsta, Hamnavoe, Burravoe, Otterswick, Colvister. There was a Samphrey Island containing in its appearance and its name the essence of this liquid world where the land rises from the water like dark jewels in a coloured sea.

The colours were pure and sharp, Mediterranean in intensity, but austere as though cooled and settled by the years. They were never brutal though they were strong, as though a glaze had been laid on them to deepen and intensify and preserve them.

When the weather is good most of the Scottish islands

have this intense deeply fired colour. The likening of the northern islands to those of the Mediterranean is not altogether a licence. The effect in the north is partly the washed cleanliness given by sea and wind, but the fierce light of the south and the crystal light of the north have a strangely similar quality.

There is, of course, an old tradition that links the Scottish islands with the Mediterranean. There was a pre-Christian trade, probably by the Phoenicians, with the islands of Scotland—possibly the Hebrides (the *Hebudae* of Pliny). There is an extant story, built on the folk-lore of centuries, of a 'people' who once sailed from the Iberian peninsula and colonized the islands. It crops up more as an act of imagination than as precise legend. Yet, in 1950, a prehistoric stone temple was excavated in Shetland and found to have features which have no duplicate in Europe north of Malta.

My hut on Saxa Vord in Unst was of wood, a strong two-roomed cabin anchored against the wind. In springtime there was very little mist or rain and the sun shone most days. My window faced west. In the distance, but nowhere near the limit of vision, were the West Skerries, off the mainland of Shetland. They were fifty miles away, a white streak on the water.

Below the hut the land dropped in a precipice to the sea-loch of Burra Firth. On the cliffs were tens of thousands of sea-birds. If one startled them they took off in a cloud of moving wings that obscured the sea below. The ledges were occupied mainly by guillemots and razor-bills, and there was a contingent of puffins like old crabbed parrots painted with cosmetics.

Across Burra Firth—almost a Euclidian line in having

length but no great width—was the promontory of Herma
Ness. (Herma and the Saxa of my hill were both fabulous
giants.) On the far side of Herma Ness the sea stretched to
the north of Yell. Beyond it was Yell Sound and the Point
of Fathaland on the mainland and the hills above Collafirth.
That was a good forty miles away and the Skerries lay still
farther in the distance like spume on the Atlantic. One knew
them by the white water they raised.

Every morning, over bacon and eggs, I watched this view.
The sea was alive. Near at hand—within the first twenty
miles—it turned and moved in a weaving pattern of inter-
flowing greens and blues, an arabesque of curves and volutes.
Farther away the movement grew more rigid till it was no
more significant than the moving hand of a clock. The land
shared the movement. It was flung into relief and then
diminished by the sea. Herma Ness had its own movement
when the wind stroked the acres of scrubby heath.

On some days the pervasive sea was dominated and over-
powered by the sky, when the west wind drove clouds overhead in endless legions of snow mountains. The wind blew
mightily across the Atlantic, unimpeded since it left the
Americas. It was usually a double wind. There was basically
a persistent current, far more than a breeze, a wind that
was steady and certain. It contained every now and then
a series of secondary gusts, roaring and powerful, great
bubbles of turbulence that banged and larrupped against
the cabin.

Unst had the special atmosphere of its northerliness. It
was the edge of the world where the free air and the limit-
less sea met and surrounded the naked rock. South of Saxa
Vord were arable parts where crofters tilled the land with the

old Shetland hand-plough. The fuel was peat, and driftwood when it could be gathered on the more accessible beaches. The old women were practised in the spider-fine knitting of shawls. Shetland knitting is fine enough (in Lerwick you test a large shawl by drawing it through a wedding ring). In Unst the art reached its most gossamer perfection. The wool was 'roo'ed' or plucked from the sheep instead of shorn.

It was to this island that Jean Biot came in 1817. He was professor of physical astronomy in the university of Paris and he came to conduct researches in the length of the second's pendulum. He left a record of his satisfaction with the island after the tumultuous years of Napoleon in his own land:

During the twenty-five years in which Europe was devouring herself, the sound of a drum had not been heard in Unst . . . during twenty-five years the door of the house I inhabited had remained open day and night.

In the Shetlands there is no place more than three miles from the sea. The steam-age literally touches the islands only when the steamers call. The hand-plough and the sheltered cabbage patch—small rectangles of emerald green against the wine-dark moors—have taken their place with man's most modern inventions, the wireless and the aeroplane. To many inhabitants the railway is a contrivance that they have seen only in pictures.

When the Norse kingdom collapsed in the thirteenth century only the Orkneys and Shetlands remained in Norse hands. In 1468 they were mortgaged to Scotland by King Christian of Denmark and Norway as a pledge for part of the dowry of his daughter, married to James of Scotland.

The money has never been paid and there remains the theoretical possibility that Norway might claim the islands in exchange for the outstanding sum of 8000 florins.

The Norse language survived in Shetland for centuries and remains part of the daily speech in words and idioms, especially in farming and fishing terms. Shetland, a county in its own right, is probably the only civic authority in Britain to maintain relations with a foreign power by sending good wishes to the King of Norway on his birthday. In January each year Lerwick has a festival of Up-Helly-A when citizens dressed as vikings burn a replica of a Viking ship and preserve the legend in which a dead Jarl is borne to Valhalla with his burning ship as a bier.

One of the pleasantest sights in Lerwick is offered by what a Victorian visitor called 'feathered bipeds'. The sea-gulls perch on the edge of chimney-pots, their heads to the wind, their hind-quarters settled over the rising current of hot peaty air. They have the self-indulgent solemnity of elderly gentlemen warming themselves at a club fireplace.

The Victorians, who were enthusiastic travellers, had a delightful habit of passing on private foibles as universal wisdom. One gentleman who recorded his impressions of visiting most of the islands of the Orkneys and Shetlands gave the advice that 'No one should land on any of these islands, where there is a chance of being storm-stayed for several days, or it might be, though rarely in ordinary summers, weeks, without a pocket enema.'

The three most interesting small islands are St Kilda, Foula, and Fair Isle. St Kilda is the most isolated and the last inhabitants left in 1930. The St Kilda house was a variation of the so-called 'black house' of the Highlands and Islands. The shape was squat and oval, perfect for a climate of strong winds. The stone walls were of double thickness with a layer of rammed earth between. The roof was of wood, thatched with turf, in shape somewhat like the top of a bee-hive. One traveller to St Kilda noted that the straw ropes holding the thatch were pegged with the beaks of Solan geese.

Until a hundred years ago the Western Highlands and some of the Islands were very short of nails (parts of the mainland were more inaccessible than islands that lay on shipping routes). Wood, where it existed, had to be worked roughly and secured by rope binding or wooden pegs. On a treeless coast, a shipwreck was a godsend and was often regarded as such, so that a minister might pray that if the Almighty in his wisdom should be intending to wreck a ship, the local coast could be recommended as a worthy site for the catastrophe.

The lack of nails meant that a prudent man, on a rare journey across the sea to a town, would carry nails back with him so that his own coffin could be soundly made. Many a man has refused to contemplate death until his coffin was constructed to his satisfaction, after which it might lie for years giving daily assurance of an ultimate Christian burial.

It is obvious that a technique involving the beaks of Solan geese was unlikely to survive into the twentieth century. St Kilda is deserted. Foula and Fair Isle have always been more in touch with the world. Foula is remote enough for the Norse language to have survived there until the eighteenth century. The population was then described as having 'a frank, free disposition, simple primitive manners, rendering them very amiable people', a patronizing comment which conveys the sense of superiority which visitors still bring to the islands.

On Foula and Fair Isle the way of life reaches back to the Stone Age. Some techniques—building, for example—can hardly have changed in two thousand years. In fact the 1939–45 war probably caused a greater upheaval than any other event within the last two millennia.

(One might make a marginal note that the famous Fair Isle designs are of ancient Norse origin, in spite of the popular story that relates them to Spanish sailors wrecked from the Armada.)

Nowadays the tractor has its place beside the ox in tilling the soil. A small community such as on Fair Isle is in no danger of disintegrating in the same way as that on St Kilda. The latter island was completely isolated and offered nothing of any consequence to its inhabitants except grazing for sheep. The Fair Islanders export their knitting at good prices, and import revenue to run the post office and mend the roads. The community budget balances favourably. Many of the men have travelled, seen the world, and prefer the isolation of the island.

No female children have been born to the seventy inhabitants of Fair Isle for twenty years. It is an odd biological fiat against which there is no argument. The crucial factor in a small community is the same as with a large nation. The number of able-bodied men is the exact measure of vitality. If at any time in the future Fair Isle cannot raise a crew for the small boat that goes out to meet the steamer that serves the island, then the life of the community automatically perishes and the inhabitants are bound to leave.

There are two old crofters on the island, man and wife. The old lady, a fine gentle woman, helps to drag the plough while her husband steers. She has never seen the 'north light' on the island. It is a mile or two away from her croft and she has never, in her lifetime, had occasion to go there. The 'south light' she knows. It is visible from her door.

The islands vary from one to another so much that one cannot write comprehensively of them. The Orkneys, for example, are a prosperous group where the modern ways of egg and poultry production and the use of the aeroplane as a means of swift marketing have made a haven of plenty between the depopulated Highlands and the more spartan régime of the Shetlands.

In Skye the crofters battled ruggedly last century in their fight against landlord and state. In the end they won their fight but only after an incredible piece of folly on the part of the Victorian statesman, Gladstone, who sent marines to the island. The Battle of the Braes does not figure largely in the history of Victorian England but it is interesting that a Liberal Prime Minister found it necessary to have guns fired against men who claimed nothing but the right to till their native land. To live on islands is to be misunderstood in cities.

The Hebrides have suffered from the technicolor writing of romantic travellers. A Lewisman gave me a verbal note on the Hebrides: 'On the one hand there is the ecstatic unreality of the misty isles of the west. On the other there is the perpetual vituperative warfare between sects of Protestants and Catholics, a hypocritical religiosity with sour-faced "Wee Free" ministers battling for souls against the sleek devils of Popery. The people themselves? They don't like work any more than you or I do. They also manage to die in greater numbers in Britain's wars than any other people. I blame that not on a foolish patriotism or on the machinations of the Navy and the War Office. Since the '45, all the way through the generations of aggressive bullying and murdering landlords, you have had a special attitude develop towards "authority". Wave a red flag in the Hebrides and men will follow you to Peru and fight for you and die for you. They're not pugnacious. They're really very mild, but they fall into step by second nature. It's less than a hundred years since the great evictions when people watched their houses being burned by "authority". That sort of thing does something to people. The best that can happen to the Hebrides is a suspension of activity by church and state. Let the people find themselves again, free of "authority".'

There was a great deal of 'that sort of thing'. The modern traveller may, or may not, find it. But to understand it there are two thousand years of history to unravel, layer upon layer of interpenetrating culture. The islander is the heir of the two greatest civilizations that northern Europe produced before the Middle Ages—the Celts and the Norse.

It would be unfair to leave it there. The traditional independence of the Highlander is fortified by isolation, and is probably stronger and more stubborn on islands than on the more accessible mainland. This independence is a human quality, and like other attitudes maintained in life it has to be supported by food and clothing and warm housing. If the islander sees that economic factors are against him he uproots himself entirely and emigrates, rather than alter his way of life in his homeland.

Outsiders, long ago conditioned to accept factories and staggered hours, queues and bustle, as the norm of living often fail to understand the Highlanders and Islanders to whom time is a commodity to be used sparingly and a lifetime is insufficient for the contemplation that a man requires in the face of the absolute. The outsider considers the Islander to be behind the times, a little shiftless in a charming way, extremely slow to improving his lot, and lazy besides.

These *ex cathedra* judgements of an age that brings itself to early death by overwork in cities, that succumbs under the wheels of its juggernauts of travel, that has lost the art of leisure and the very taste for quiet good living, are received with polite distaste in the Islands where they order things differently. The most notorious attempt to improve the lot of the 'poor crofter' was made in the island of Harris by Lord Leverhulme. The defeat of the noble Lord by the crofters was described by George Blake as 'one of the most significant episodes in Scottish history'.

Lord Leverhulme's idea was to construct new buildings so that tweed weaving could be organized commercially instead of being conducted piece-meal on hand-looms in crofts. He also wanted to tackle the fishing trade and put it on a sound economic footing. He built a factory. He built model houses to be occupied by his workers. His scheme was a sound and realistic mixture of business and philanthropy, and the islanders were quite aware that it would put more butter on their bread. On the other hand, the price to be paid for the benefits of steady work, wages and a new house, was the loss of their island independence. Why should they, as their spokesman said, give away their right of individual living within sound of the waves in exchange for disciplined hours as paid workers and the terrible authority of the factory bell?

The traveller to these northern isles will be unconcerned with those nice problems arising out of the past. What he is more likely to appreciate is the lovely scenery of unbelievable beauty, the sweet trout of Shetland, the home-cured hams of Orkney, the tremendous heartening potages of mutton that are served on the ship crossing the Minch to Stornoway. In the 'simmer dim' the cathedral of Kirkwall and the Standing Stones of Treshnish are annealed with the green of the *machair* and the swart moors into an exile's dream of home.

Chapter Six

TO SAIL THE SEAS

KIPLING KNEW ENOUGH OF the Scots, and sufficient of the old 'up-and-down' marine engine, to make his Scots engineer see

Predestination in the stride o' yon connectin'-rod.

McAndrew in his *Hymn* does not regard the universe as an elaborately functional piece of machinery. But he does believe that his propeller-driving contraption of steam and steel and oil, beating across the seven seas and back again, contains exactly the same mystery as the vault of heaven, and for that reason is to be adored with a rough practical tenderness, but not worshipped in idolatry, and certainly not despised as a 'mere machine'. When, in parts of *McAndrew's Hymn*, the old chief sups the cold porridge of Presbyterian conscience and guilt he is probably less Scots and more Kipling.

Kipling was a favourite (along with Conrad and Jack London) of the sea-going Scots a generation ago, and I am told he is still stowed under the bunks of the men of the watch below. My own copy of *McAndrew's Hymn* has pencilled marginal notes made at sea. Kipling's 'Oiler!' is corrected to 'Greaser!' and the line 'When I go testin' follower-bolts' is marked with the comment 'What a funny chief!'

But if Kipling nodded over a few technicalities, his general appreciation of machinery is approved.

> *. . . the feed-pump sobs an' heaves*
> *An' now the main eccentrics start their quarrel on the sheaves:*
> *Her time, her own appointed time, the rocking link-head bides,*
> *Till—hear that note?—the rod's return whings glimmerin'*
> *   through the guides.*
> *They're all awa! True beat, full power, the clangin' chorus goes*
> *Clear to the tunnel where they sit, my purrin' dynamos.*
> *Interdependence absolute, foreseen, ordained, decreed,*
> *To work, ye'll note, at any tilt an' every rate o' speed.*

There one has it. The practical detail and the universal, the physics and the metaphysics, comprehended together. If one can elaborate the attitude without drowning it with explanations it is the combination of the Celt and the Saxon, the Highlander and the Lowlander, that has made the Scottish engineer. Tradition has it that if you call down the engine-room hatch of any ship at sea a Scots voice will answer. Within that exaggeration there is the suggestion that a very great number of marine engineers are Scots. And so it is, and the pity in the past was that so many were forced to sea in the way their brothers were forced to emigrate, because there was no living at home.

The Scots are no more sea-loving than their neighbours. (One needs a different climate to become enamoured of the ocean.) But they are sea-going. There is an instinct for the sea and a tradition of seamanship that came with the Scandinavians one and a half thousand years ago.

Peter F. Anson in his book *Scots Fisherfolk* points out that there are two attitudes towards the sea in Scotland, the Norse and the Celtic. On the East Coast, where the Lowlander lives, there is a fear of the sea. Life is 'bound up with taboos and superstitions', with pagan beliefs that are now vanishing but were very strong until quite recently. But the sea 'is a source of wealth waiting to be claimed by any man who has the daring'.

The West Coast man, the Celt, was 'far more conscious of the mystery of the ocean—she was a spirit that had to be wooed'. We find here, as in many other aspects of Scottish life, the two predominant types of Scotsmen. The Lowlander, in answer to the challenge of circumstance, becomes practical and ingenious, dourly persistent. He invents and dares. The Highlander, accepting his inherited role, wonders and worships and aspires, and acquires sufficient technical skill to see him through his days, but he does not elaborate and create new things. He might make a poem, but not a machine.

When these two attitudes coalesce they give birth to an inventive fervour, an aspiring practicality, which knows no bounds. This union of abilities and outlooks produced the early technicians and inventors who created the age of steam. One does not wish to become lost in a world of romantic anthropology, but the amalgam of Highlander and Lowlander is the most important thing that has happened in Scotland. Time and time again it is found behind the undertakings in which the Scots have been particularly adept— in electro-magnetics, in surgery, in civil engineering, in shipping and steam engineering. These technical sciences were developed in their infancy by the panache of Celtic imagination and the patient inventiveness of the Lowlander. It is astonishing how many of the most eminent men in the different fields bore Highland names. Many of them had 'lost the Gaelic'. They came from the Highlands, or their parents had come from the Highlands, and they pursued their studies and crafts in the Lowland cities. McAndrew himself, the ocean-going chief engineer, is a humble, fictitious and modern example. One feels that if McAndrew had not been born too late he would have invented the engines and the ship to hold them as well as sailing as chief.

From the early days of the *Comet* in 1812, battering its paddles against the waves of the Firth of Clyde, to the twentieth-century *Queens*, the newest, biggest and safest ships have been the product of this fruitful combination of Highlander and Lowlander. One needed other things in the beginning. One needed an age of development, one needed the intermingling of peoples that followed the 1745 rebellion and the 'settling' of the Highland question. One needed coal, an iron-smelting industry, and excellent wrights in the blacksmiths' shops. One also needed a great experimental inland waterway, part river and part sea. Those conditions were satisfied and the ancestors of McAndrew, the Lowland-speaking Highlander, provided the ships and the whole cavalcade of machines that move by steam. It is of incidental interest, but hardly sufficient to defend a thesis, that the Clyde itself is Highland on one side and Lowland on the other.

The greater number of Scottish seamen neither build ships nor sail in them across the seas of the world. They sleep at home, now and then, and go to the fishing. In proportion to the population there are seven times more fishermen in Scotland than in England. There are over three hundred fishing stations and ports in the country. The fishermen are probably the worst paid of our food producers. They live— and frequently die—in conditions that are arduous at the best of times and purgatory at the worst.

The toughest of the fishermen breed were the deep-sea Shetland fishers of last century. In their 'sixerns' they crossed the shallow shelf of the North Sea into the Atlantic depths. They stayed away for days, and when they raised the hill of Saxa Vord on the way back they knew their navigation was good. They carried food and drink and peat for making a fire. The 'sixern' was an open boat, with no deck or shelter whatsoever. It had six oars and one square sail. It went out of use in the late nineties but its small brother, the 'fourareen', is still fishing the Shetland waters.

Deep-sea trawlers now go inside the Arctic Circle. The herring-drifters follow the shoals that move down the sea lanes on both sides of the country. But the type of man who for centuries passed on the tradition of seafaring is becoming rarer. Deep-sea fishing is a modern technique developed out of steam. It feeds the huge maws of the cities. The 'professional' has taken over from the crofter-fisherman whose way of life was a seasonal gamble of food-gathering and food-production—a little 'bere' or thin barley, cabbages, potatoes, lobsters, white fishing, whisky, sheep, deer. Whatever the land and the sea provided made his meagre living.

It was the Highlander who turned fishing and crofting into a regular pattern of life. The Highland community was a closed society, a fascinating mixture of individualism and co-operation. A man's cow was his own, and what he grew on his patch, but he went with his neighbour to the fishing because at least two pairs of arms were needed, one to row and the other to handle the lines. The crofter, with his cow and share of a boat, would be beholden to no man, not even his neighbour, but in a social sense the scattered community to which he belonged was knit with an almost tribal code. They were the people of such and such a bay. Most of them had the same surname. They maintained out of very ancient times a fund of legend, an inheritance of land and sea skills, and a language which was attuned to a mystic intimacy with the natural world.

Fishing as a trade is very ancient and was conducted mostly by the Lowland part of the country where the coast had been settled by Scandinavians. In the Middle Ages the church had control of salmon fisheries, a right granted by the Scottish Kings. At the same period, dried herring went south in vast quantities. Long after the Reformation the Scots traders, if not the fishers, became prosperous on the needs of Catholic countries. Scots herring in barrels went to Spain, to the Baltic and the Hanseatic ports.

The long history of fishing on the East Coast has brought into the present day a survival of superstitions. In a few estuaries where salmon fishing is carried on, it is usual to have a religious service at the beginning of the season when the nets are blessed by a minister. But the sea-fisherman is wary of the power of the Church. A new boat is very rarely blessed. This may be because the medieval Church never had vested rights in what was caught at sea. It makes a neat comment on the positive and negative responses to the supernatural. But on shore the sea-fisherman, during last century, showed himself to be particularly susceptible to the waves of evangelism that swept his villages.

The east coast fishing communities are rapidly losing their individuality. This century, with the brisk action of a hygienic broom, has swept away the rags and tatters of old beliefs that had survived from pagan times. As always happens, picturesque local customs have vanished as well. At one time a marriage at Collieston on the coast of Aberdeenshire was celebrated on the links when the 'Lang Reel o' Collieston' was danced

on the greensward under the blue canopy of heaven on a sweet afternoon in summer . . . the music of the violin, the song of the lark in mid-heaven right overhead, the ringing guffaws of the juvenile spectators, the clapping of hands, the loud 'hoochs' and 'whoops' of the dancing fishermen, all commingling and commingled with the murmur of the billows breaking among the rocks . . .

The description from the *Banffshire Journal* has idyllic overtones but one notes the accurate record of the guffaws.

Ullapool, the small fishing port in Wester Ross, looks like a model town built in newly explored territory. The streets are laid in rectangles. The solitary T-shaped pier juts into the water of Loch Broom. The main store is entitled in bold letters 'The Loch Broom Trading Company'. The old stone cottages are whitewashed. The new houses are of wood and give a pioneering Hudson Bay atmosphere.

Below the piles of the pier the sea-bed is covered with a pulp of rotting mackerel. These fish are still considered unclean and are flung overboard from the ships. When the herring boats come in, the streets are busy with men in thigh boots, with girls from the open-air curing stations, with truck drivers ready to haul the fish over the long route to the south across the high land of the Dirrie Mhor. There is no railway at Ullapool. The hills of Ross are folded down the sides of Loch Broom like high petrified waves.

When the boats are unloaded they sometimes turn about and make for the open sea. They sail down Loch Broom and from high ground they look like small brown toys on a wild serpentine pond. They are making for the Hebrides, the Golden Isles of the West, and in summer when the sun is shining and the air is so still that a waterfall can be heard two miles away across the loch, visiting tourists who remember their classics think of the Hesperides.

The boats sail past the small group of islands that are called the Summer Isles. They finally vanish from sight, unless you climb still higher when they are brought back into view like small dark corks, and the Hebrides themselves are seen, a band of purple darkness on the horizon. The town of Ullapool on its spit of green land has become a small white geometrical design.

The boats are off to Stornoway, fifty miles distant, some-where in the band of purple. The boats are in a hurry—their dispersed smoke drifts near the Summer Isles like a detached squall of rain—because there is a day or two of leisure before putting to sea again in search of the herring shoals. The crews do not come from the Highlands but from the East Coast of Scotland. They could stay at Ullapool if they wished during the days off-duty, but they prefer Stornoway in the Golden Isles of the West. There is a picture house there.

Chapter Seven

TO CONSIDER ORIGINS

Most holy Father and Lord, we know and gather from ancient Acts and Records, that in every famous nation this of Scotland hath been celebrate with many praises. This nation having come from Scythia the Greater, through the Tuscan Sea, and the Hercules Pillars, and having for many ages taken its residence in Spain in the midst of a most fierce people, could never be brought in subjection by any people how barbarous soever; and having removed from these parts, above 1200 years after the coming of the Israelites out of Egypt, did by many victories and much toil obtain these parts in the West which they still possess, having expelled the British and entirely rooted out the Picts, notwithstanding the frequent assaults and invasions they met with from the Norwegians, Danes, and English; and these parts and possessions they have always retained free from all manner of servitude and subjection, as ancient Histories do witness.

From the Declaration of Arbroath, 1320, a letter sent from the Scottish People to the Pope in his role of International Arbitrator.

THE SCHOOL INSPECTOR STOOD before a class of children in Aberdeen. He smiled encouragement. 'You,' he said, pointing. 'Can you tell me who were the early inhabitants of Scotland?'

The little girl thought for a moment. Obviously she was not certain though she was not stumped. Then, in a burst of confidence, she shouted, 'The wee dark men, mister'.

The class did not laugh. They accepted it.

'You mean the Picts?' said the inspector.

'Yes, mister, the Picts, the wee dark men.'

Every country fondles its own idea of a Golden Age in the very distant past. Some anthropologists encourage it by discussing early civilizations that were quite peaceful until the evolution of society produced separate states governed by kings. Kings became rivals and needed warriors, and so the armed soldier, with all the brutal consequences of his calling, entered history at a definite period of development. The Golden Age was over.

An ancient period of peace and plenty is a popular concept in Scottish lore—that is, in the mixture of Celtic, Norse and Anglian legend that invests the country with an involved variety of origins. One writer rather regretfully relinquishes the idea of a Celtic Golden Age, remarking that the Celts must have changed mightily by the time the Romans came. Even the hardened troops of Rome's imperialism were daunted by the methods the natives had of dealing with prisoners of war. 'Ferocious but likeable,' said Tacitus more moderately.

The Celts, who came to Britain from the Continent in two major waves, had been a very civilized people. The distinguishing feature of the Celts was not physical. They were a body of peoples speaking the same language. Their very great civilization has survived to this day, though what is left on the sea-girt promontories of Britain and France is a poor travesty of what existed when the Celts were the peaceful masters of Europe.

They laid down methods of law and government that permeate French practice to this day. When the Romans conquered Gaul they did not attempt to destroy the Celtic way of life. The Roman speech was imposed slowly and French developed out of Latin as a Celtic modification. The turn of sentences, the use of demonstratives, the character of the verbs, are common to French and to the Celtic languages.

No true Celtic state has survived. Scottish Gaeldom is a ghost and Ireland is a new creation. When, in the 1880's, British rifles were fired against the crofters of Skye the event made a modern tail-piece to the most consistent part of Europe's history—the decline of the Celts for two thousand years. Those who are now peasant fishers and crofters on the western peninsulas and islands of Scotland are the modern remnants of a civilized aristocracy in Europe to which we owe much of the sensibility and humanity that is essentially European.

But where was the Golden Age? Recent investigations in

southern Scotland show that there was once a civilization which was undisturbed by war and evidently quite ignorant of it. The Bronze Age in the Borders was somewhat later than in the south, and during it, from about 900 to 400 B.C. there was a continuing community of people, many thousands strong, who apparently lived peacefully, tilled their fields, hunted game. In such a long quiet period of five hundred years there would be a great development of religion and art. The people have left no signs of defence works and they built no hill-top forts. They lived in the valleys and there are no weapons amongst the tools and appliances that have survived.

They may have been Celts, Gaels or Brythons. They may not. They may have been Picts, for the Picts were of the same period. But the Picts themselves may have been Brythonic Celts. The girl who was questioned by the school-inspector knew of the Picts but she preferred her 'wee dark men'.

The small dark men, whoever they were, still live in popular fancy, especially in country districts. They may have been quite legendary. They come to the tongue of people who have never heard of the Picts, but there are people who think the Picts and the small dark men were one and the same. The tradition of small dark men is the imaginative force within John Buchan's weird and frightening book *The Watcher by the Threshold*, a story of small people who lived underground in Galloway. The Picts and the small men survive in the imagination, undefined, unidentified, and certainly unpacific, as the mysterious ancestors of the Scots. They may have been the original Caledonians and presumably they were stern and wild. Later came the Celts, and much later still the Norse and the Angles, all contributing a great deal to what Scotland is to-day.

A tradition of small men, dwarfs and troglodytes, might have arisen quite easily. Assume, for a minute, a modern world without communications. It would be easy for a legend to arise concerning the French of whom it is said that they drink wine and are somewhat short of average western stature. The French, quite easily, become pygmies who live on berry-juice.

In Scotland as elsewhere the story-teller down the centuries was the source of social entertainment. He was also official historian. He mingled fact with fiction to suit his audience or his own temperament. When he had completed his repertoire he relied on his imagination to embellish what had already been said. A story would reappear in a new guise. The important central characters would be given new exploits. Stories would be chopped and changed. New tales, heard far away, would be incorporated. In time all the variations became embodied in the community's store of legend. And this legend was the history of the people.

Hollywood does the same to-day, having taken over very exactly the role of tribal story-teller. Fortunately, history and entertainment have been separated. The difference between a folk-story and reality is very much the same as between an average American film and 'real life', with the exception that the old story-teller was often a great artist.

Where the Picts are concerned, if one cuts away the more ornate trimmings, there is nothing left except the persistent 'small dark men'. Archaeologists offer one explanation.

Prehistoric burial grounds, or cairns, were sometimes in the shape of small chambers of stone, perhaps two feet high. Later peoples, coming upon these and not understanding them, thought they were houses. A large cairn, containing a number of chambers, was interpreted as a village of minute vanished people. There are many such cairns on the Orkneys, and Orcadian folk-lore is rich in stories of small men.

Dwarfs run through Gaelic legend. One tale is of a person of normal stature surrounded by dwarfs who threatened to eat his flesh and drink his blood. The hero picks up one of the dwarfs—'the largest of head and the thinnest of shank'— and uses the fellow as a weapon against his small adversaries, to the ultimate destruction of all the dwarfs.

Variations of this tale are found in different parts of Scotland and similar stories occur in the folk-lore of other continents. The small men appear to have been pandemic.

Scottish legend identifies these dwarfish cannibals as pre-Celtic thus putting them in the time of the Picts who are also called troglodytes. Adam of Bremen in the eleventh century writes of dwarfish 'Fenlanders' who lived 'in caves of the rocks, which they quitted at night-time for the purpose of committing sanguinary outrages'. Orkney had a fifteenth-century story on the same lines and in this the dwarfs were labelled 'Peihts, Picts or Piks'. They were also the *Peti*. Thus we have the Pentland, or Pictland Firth, between Orkney and the mainland, and the Pentland hills near Edinburgh.

The fifteenth-century Orcadian tradition in all probability was Norse. Only then were the Norse modifying their claim to ownership of the island. The story said that, six centuries before, the inhabitants of the islands were *Pape*, dwarfs or

Picts. These must have been the people found by the original Norse conquerors, or else they were the imaginary inhabitants of the prehistoric cairns. From an Irish source we find that in Orkney the Norse discovered the *Pape* or Christian men—early Christian fathers or popes of the Culdee Church. They could not tolerate the heathen seaman and quietly withdrew from the islands. It is most unlikely that these Culdee priests were cannibalistic or dwarfish. And thus the Picts or the small dark men retreat once again into their mystery.

Yet there is consistency. Saint Columba, who brought Christianity from Ireland to Scotland, was a great-grandson of Connal Gulban who is reputed to have battled with a race of dwarfs. Columba's followers—the Irish Gaels who were the *Pape*—are said to have lived in Orkney with a race of dwarfs who were famous as builders. Here we come upon the stone-age style of building which is still prevalent in the islands, the enduring solid structure which weathers centuries. And so we arrive again, like people repeating their errors in a maze, at the prehistoric cairns with their small 'dwarfish' chambers.

If the Christian *Pape* were conquerors of the older *Peti*, or Picts (dwarfish or not), then the Norse may well have confused the two in their later legends. We also find that the dwarfs who were conquered by Connal Gulban were described, in an Irish version, as *Cruithne* which is the usual Scots Gaelic term for the 'pre-Celtic' Picts in Scotland. It is the *Cruithne* who still exist in the imagination of the Scots as the 'small dark men'.

In this mystery, which is still transmitted in oral legend, the only thing that emerges with certainty is that the interlocking stories are concerned with an ancient struggle between Gaelic Celts and the Picts.

There are scholars who say that the Picts spoke a non-Celtic and non-Indo-European language. In the north of Scotland, particularly in the Shetlands, there is a variety of Ogam script (the utility alphabet of the Celts of the sixth century) which is Pictish.

The word Pict became a general term for the inhabitants of Scotland 'beyond the wall'. It may be that the people who opposed the Romans were the mysterious early race. But the small dark men are of an older period. Who they were is still unknown. It is strange how they have persisted in the mists of racial memory. The modern schoolgirl in her pre-cast concrete classroom, member of a junior film club, bebop fan and hockey player, is aware of her ancestors.

'Why do you call them wee dark men?' asked the inspector, encouraging the girl.

'I don't know.' She was a little embarrassed at being kept the centre of attention.

The inspector was kindly. 'Where did you hear about them?'

But the girl was confused. 'I don't know. I just heard tell o' them,' she mumbled.

The inspector smiled quietly to himself. It was just as it should be. One doesn't teach about the small dark men. But they come down the generations, from mouth to mouth and mind to mind, and no one quite knows how he has learned about them.

Chapter Eight

PRUD'HOMME

TO SUP WITH THE DEVIL

Rowan-tree and red thread
Will put the witches to their speed.

IT WAS J. B. PRIESTLEY who said of Robert Louis
Stevenson that he was, like a true Scotsman, 'on nodding
terms at least with the Devil'. The Scottish Devil is a man of
ancient pedigree, and only in a very puritan conscience does
he become confused with the relative newcomer, Satan. He
is no proud Lucifer but an engagingly uproarious and pleasantly dissolute rogue. He has none of the arrogance of a
fallen angel and is only too human in his love of wild parties.
But he is also an 'awful warning', a black sheep who will
weep tears of repentance on your shoulder while his hand
skilfully picks your pocket.

Side by side with the Devil sits the grinning skull of

Death, another old familiar. The two are cronies, who are treated sometimes with the greatest disrespect, sometimes with a sublime awe, but rarely with the petrified fear and abasement to which they are accustomed in some other countries.

There is a man who lives in a pleasant house on a Border hill-side. His bookshelves are filled with volumes of Scottish history and literature. With quiet hospitality he shares his pleasures, offering a jar of tobacco and a perusal of a first edition of the Border Minstrelsy, always ready to embark on an informed discussion of a minor point in history. He cultivates his Scottishness as other people cultivate their gardens. Amongst the things he has collected in a long life is a number of photographs, taken by himself, of old Scottish gravestones. The carvings on them are interesting. A skull bares its teeth in an eternal smile: a skeleton stands with its feet on a skull flanked by cross-bones and crossed shovels, an hour-glass and a bell; a skeleton is accompanied by two children. These are grimly honest symbols of mortality. They are almost homely, showing little terror of mortal corruption. How unlike the great Byzantine mosaics where the skeletons become the haunt of plump worms that wriggle from eyeless sockets, where a consummate art has transformed the natural biology of death into an obsessive spiritual torment.

There is on the surface a mixture of indifference and callousness, sometimes of sentimentality, in the Lowland attitude towards death. Personal grief is turned inwards. It is the habit of the people, like the soldier biting on the bullet. There is no public lamentation.

So, when a poet like Dunbar ends each stanza of a poem

with the line *Timor Mortis conturbat me*, it has the effect of a clapper falling on the bell of doom. Dunbar is at one end of the scale. The dancing skeletons are somewhere in the middle, and at the other extreme are the popular jokes of modern Scottish music halls, where a comedian can rouse his audience to gales of ghoulish laughter and oceans of merry tears with jokes about funerals and 'deceaseds' that stun a stranger into amazed horror.

There is a story, not of the music halls, which some do not find funny, but which is a pointer to a way of looking at things.

A laird called Garscadden was entertaining a number of friends in his country home. It was the days of three-bottle men and bachelor parties. The company, toss-pots all, were ready to carry on till the guttering candles were extinguished by dawn. A magnificent dinner was followed by hours of conviviality. Midnight came and went. Wine and stories filled the night. When a man crashed from his chair the servants put him to bed if they could not revive him. About four in the morning a guest happened to glance below the vast table and saw that his host was lying prostrate, not looking at all well. The guest turned to a neighbour.

'Whit maks Garscadden luik sae gash?' (look so pale)

The other man held a finger to his lips: 'Whisht? Not a word to the others! It's a corpse below the table. Garscadden's been dead these twa-three hours and he himself would not have liked his death to spoil the merriment.'

This story may seem to be macabre flippancy but it has a pith of Scottishness that cannot be ignored. Death and merriment often went together and a funeral was also a revel, a *danse funèbre*. A visitor in the eighteenth century declared 'a Scots funeral to be merrier than an English wedding'. Pennant, writing of the Highlands in the same period, relates that on the evening after a death there was a dance in the deceased's house, and though the dance started in a melancholy way it developed into such gambols and frolics that 'the loss which occasioned them is more than supplied by the consequences of that night'. One also remembers the Highland funeral scene in *Humphrey Clinker* in which the company mourns so effectively that when they arrive at church they find they have forgotten the body.

But it is the Devil himself who comes roistering into Scottish company with the persistent impudence of a circus clown. To the man in the street, should he ever think of him at all nowadays, the Devil has emerged from the years as a 'couthie body'. Auld Nick, auld Clootie and a score of familiar by-names show that he has a warm if uncertain place in the hearts of the Scots. Compared with the Scottish Church in the days of its termagant power the Devil was a friend, and something of that remains.

There is nothing very unusual in Scottish legends about the Devil unless it is that in the end the creature becomes a laughing-stock. In folk-lore he frequently appears disguised as a mortal, usually bungling the job on hand. As a carpenter he cuts wood so badly that he harms himself: he muffs his work as a tinker; he botches a job as a farrier; when working as a tailor he cuts cloth so badly that his master stabs him with a bodkin. Even in Hell he is not much of a success so that his master Vulcan says there is nothing he can do but 'blow the bellows and piss among the coals'. A poor chap, this Devil. But he seems to have had success and encouragement as a piper and musician, with plenty of practice at such social gatherings as the witches' dance in Kirk Alloway.

> *Warlocks and witches in a dance;*
> *Nae cotillon brent new frae France,*
> *But hornpipes, jigs, strathspeys, and reels,*
> *Put life and mettle in their heels.*
> *At winnock-bunker in the east,*
> *There sat auld Nick, in shape o' beast:*
> *A towzie tyke, black, grim, and large;*
> *To gie them music was his charge.*

The Scottish Devil has a mixed ancestry. He survives from the ancient pagan religions. Christianity tried to relegate him to folk-lore and the smaller magic of country credulity. But the Devil would not be supplanted by the more ominous Satan. Naturally the Scottish Devil and Satan became confused one with the other in the public mind.

When the scourge of witchcraft trials swept Scotland in the seventeenth and eighteenth centuries it was the Devil who was the butt of an orgy of vicious murder by Church and State. The practice of witchcraft rites, the joining of witches's 'covens' or gatherings, were a protest against the harsh zealousness and joylessness of the Presbyterian Church. By forbidding people to be human and merry the Church encouraged witchcraft. Many of the devilish observances were little more than the guilty strivings of honest people to fling off the burden of repression and frustration that had been loaded on them by their kirk. In order to eat, drink and

be merry, to dance and make love, they had to abandon
Puritan society and sign a coven or pact with the Devil (there
were thirteen in a 'coven' and thirteen is still the Devil's
dozen). The Church stamped this down with the fury of a
man destroying a viper. But the less tolerant the Church
was, the more the underground cults persisted. The
witches' covens drew on reserves of folk-lore and the
remnants of ancient beliefs that lingered in both town
and country. (It would be difficult to say that they are yet
quite extinct.)

Religious and secular power were intermingled in an
absolute authority over life and death, with the same appalling result that has recently been repeated in other European
countries. People informed on their neighbours. Professional
witch-finders (witch-prickers) set themselves up in office, to
their own profit. Methods of determining who was a witch
(or a warlock) were so crude and so biased that little more
than an irresponsible accusation of guilt was sufficient to
send a person to the stake. Private careers were furthered by
the judicious disposal of enemies, petty tyrants in towns and
villages disposed of those of whom they disapproved with
the thoroughness of an S.S. man in a ghetto. The foulest
tortures were part and parcel of this religious sadism.

They prickit her body from head to heel
to find the witchmark out.

One writer says:

In no country in Europe did the belief in witches and
warlocks flourish more widely, more intensely, and more
tenaciously than in Scotland. In contradistinction to the
essentially demoniac and almost scientific nature of the belief
in Germany and France, in Scotland it was altogether more

exuberant and imaginative. Here we had the 'weird sisters', who romantically voyaged across the seas in sieves, rode through the air on bean-straws, boars and bourtries, and were in direct contact and on equal terms of familiarity with the Queen of Fairy and the Devil himself.

There is a point there. There were three worlds: the mortal world, the severe eternal world of the churches, and the 'other world' in which fairies and goblins, devils and witches were mixed pell-mell. Until quite recently it was possible to believe in all three—a much richer experience, presumably, than is offered to the man of formal religion who believes in the first two, or to the atheist who can stomach only one and that with argument.

Another aspect of the witch-trials which has its present-day parallel is the way in which accused persons often confessed readily and willingly, though such a confession automatically earned the death penalty. It was a superstitious age, so it is less astonishing that ignorant country women, brought up from the cradle on a diet of crude magic, should confess to consorting with the devil, than that the accusers, sometimes men of unusual breadth of learning, should themselves believe in the charges. Women described passionately how they had been turned into flying mares, had sailed on broomsticks and had performed other miracles of locomotion. One of the most popular confessions was to have slept with the Devil. At that time the Devil fathered an extraordinary number of Scottish bairns. A great many discharged soldiers and other gay sparks travelled the country putting shrewd devilish propositions to attractive unsophisticated women. Behind the more elaborate orgies, there was a deliberate development of the theme of the story of

Boccaccio, in which, it will be remembered, Rustico, a monk, instructs the gentle Alibech in the celestial art of putting the Devil into Hell.

The mother witch is a legendary, grey-mantled woman, apparently having her origin in the south-west of Scotland. She was the Gyre Carline or Nicniven, a Hecate of the countryside. She survived for a long time as a threat to children who were warned 'McNiven'll get ye'.

Rites and ceremonies were involved before an initiate could be accepted into a 'witch coven'. The Christian faith had to be renounced and this was followed by a baptism in which a new name was bestowed. A man, accepted as the Devil or acting as his *locum*, gave the new 'spirit names'. These new names might be no more than an exchange of a normal name. Margaret might be baptized Janet. But some covens exercised a pretty sense of invention. There are records of the names: Pickle-nearest-the-wind, Able-and-Stout, Over-the-Dike-with-it.

The third essential of initiation (and of much greater importance than baptism which was frequently omitted) was the branding with the Devil's mark.

The Deuill dooth lick them with his tung in some priuy parte of their bodie, before hee dooth recieue them to be his servants, which marke commonly is guien them vnder the haire in some part of their bodye, wharby it may not easily be found out or seene, although they be searched.

That was Pitcairn's version, but in time any mark was sufficient to brand a person as a witch.

A legal gentleman, attempting to break down the mystery into a forensic formula, said that the mark 'is not *per se* found relevant, except that it is confessed by them that they got that mark with their own consent, *quo casu*, it is equivalent to a paction'. The marks which were genuinely given to persons engaging in witchcraft were probably incised or tattooed, though this was of little comfort to persons who were falsely accused on the strength of a birth-mark or a mole or some other small abnormality.

Witchcraft persecution died in the end, after about 5000 had been killed. The last was burned in pitch in 1727. How much of the thick undergrowth of superstition remains? It is almost impossible to say. One authority calculates that by the middle of the seventeenth century only the town-dwellers and the upper classes had been converted to Christianity. Older Mithraistic beliefs lingered a long time. It is doubtful if they have entirely vanished. There are people alive who can recall 'touching' for illness, who were brought up to believe in 'dark looks', unmentionable powers and spells. In the eighteenth century men who thought they had been bewitched were still lighting fires to break the spell. The fire symbolized the sun, the source and centre of light and life. The power of 'the eye' was given by dark supernatural forces. Within recent years I have met people who had it, or believed they had it.

But the remaining country dwellers who still harbour old beliefs are less inclined to discuss them, or even betray that they have them. They are sharply suspicious of an age that meets the secrets of thousands of years with hearty incredulous laughter.

Last century a farmer within twenty miles of Edinburgh

(a man who was described as 'a relative of Professor Simpson', the latter presumably the discoverer of chloroform) was known to have sacrificed a live cow 'to the spirit of the murrain'. Truth and superstition are very difficult to distinguish. Nowadays, in hygienic rectitude, we offer up when necessary a whole herd of cows to the 'spirit' of foot and mouth disease and our modern priests, the civil servants and the scientists, ensure that this sacrifice is not neglected under penalty of law.

Last century it was the custom to drag a mad person round an island in Loch Maree in the West Highlands. The unfortunate was tied to a rope and dragged behind a boat, widdershins. This was done three times to complete the cure. It is interesting as a primitive example of shock therapy.

Last century . . . but what of this century? What of the present day. When I was a child a servant used to threaten me with a visitation of the 'black man'. Probably she didn't believe in the black man: but, like a gene missing a generation, belief was born in me for a few agonized nights.

There are many who are influenced by old beliefs; there are certainly thousands who indulge innocent variations of old practices. Every May Day, the Celtic Beltane or spring festival, there is a pilgrimage in Edinburgh to the top of Arthur's Seat where, at dawn, a Christian minister conducts a service. The congregation is largely of young girls who have come to anoint themselves with dew, the time-honoured purpose of the visit. Spring, fertility, the search for a mate, the winning of personal beauty, all the ancient elements are there. When the girls have patted their faces with dew and giggled a great deal they go home and then to their work in shops and factories. They go through the rite with no knowledge of its immemorial implications. The presence of the minister shows the equally immemorial attempts of a new belief to incorporate an old one.

Just over a hundred years ago the Arthur Seat observances were nearer the original saturnalia.

In the course of half an hour the entire hill is a moving mass of all sorts and sizes. At the summit may be seen a company of bakers and other craftsmen, dressed in kilts, dancing round a Maypole. On the more level part 'next door', is usually an itinerant vendor of whiskey, or mountain (not May) dew, your approach to whom is always indicated by the number of 'bodies' carelessly lying across his path, not dead, but drunk.

Walter Scott carefully noted that dew collected on the first of May was supposed to confer witch power on the gatherer and give protection against the evil eye.

I know an outstanding Cambridge scholar who, he claims, danced on a country road in Argyll with a *revenant* on New Year's Eve of 1950. The occasion may explain the occurrence, and there are people who say a Cambridge man will believe anything.

There is plenty of material in Scotland for those who pursue occult research. Apparently sane and civilized men every now and then find giant footsteps in the snow of the Cairngorms. There is one splendid woman who specializes in exorcizing gremlins and such-like creatures, especially when they inhabit well-appointed country houses. And there is the Loch Ness monster.

The Devil himself probably knows where it will all end.

Whether he is real or not remains a moot point. He might pop up beside a lonely ploughman or nudge a man in a city pub. The Scottish conscience permits a variety of unusual phenomena. As far as his livelihood is concerned, the Devil now earns it in pantomime, and the footlights show him with an assorted company of fairies and witches, regulated by Equity.

It was a Scottish author, disappointed at the waning power of the 'other world', who reopened for children its miraculous but carefully selected delights under the guidance of Tinker Bell.

Chapter Nine

P REDHOMME

TO PUT BUTTER IN A HORSE'S EAR

> *Gug-gug said the cuckoo*
> *On the yellow day of Beltane,*
> *Gug-gug said she again,*
> *On Midsummer day.*

T HE SCOTTISH YEAR BEGINS and ends with fire
festivals. In January, towards the end of the month, the
men of Lerwick, in Viking dress, celebrate Up-Helly-A by
setting fire to a model Viking galley in the harbour waters.
At Burghead on the Moray coast the 'clavie' is burned, with
a multitude of small detail that is scrupulously observed.
This happens on the 12th, the date of the old New Year.
The clavie is made from tar and herring barrels. A stone is
used instead of a hammer. The nails and such tools as are

required must be borrowed, nothing bought. The long keynail is specially made for the day by a local smith. The clavie is a heavy and cumbersome structure including, at the top, a half barrel filled with sticks and tar. This is set alight. A man's shoulders are inserted in the under-structure of spars and the clavie is carried in triumph through the streets while flaming tar falls on the man underneath.

Throughout the year countless towns and villages have their own little celebrations and festivals, some of them reaching without a break into antiquity, some of them revived versions of earlier festivals, and a few of them quite new (instituted in envy of happier towns) but based as firmly as possible on history and legend.

In Fisherrow, the fishing village near Edinburgh, there is a fisherman's 'walk' on the second Friday of every September. The women dress in vivid traditional costume. With the men and the children and the town band they parade through the streets on holiday, carrying small dolls that are also dressed like the 'fisher-wifies'.

At South Queensferry in July a man in tight-fitting clothes is covered from head to foot with 'burrs' of the burdock plant. The burryman is then bedecked 'with flowers and ribbons, wears a head-dress of flowers and carries in each hand a staff decorated with flowers and leaves'. His function is not known. He has appeared for centuries but there are no records of his origin. During his tour of the streets he will speak to no one. It has been suggested that he is a fantastic floral variant of the 'burgh-law' man who, from his intimate knowledge of local affairs, made an annual tour of the burgh boundaries to maintain the burgh land in possession of the citizens. If this is so, then the solitary prickly burryman is the South Queensferry equivalent of the Border Common-riding celebrations.

At Lanark there is the age-old Lanimer Fair, transferred there from Berwick in 1348 when the latter town was in the hands of the English. Over one hundred town fairs had been recognized by charter before 1500 and a very great number of them still take place annually. Nearly all are in the Lowland part of Scotland. Common-ridings and other public celebrations fill the summer calendar of the Lowlands. This type of public gathering is almost unknown in the Highlands where the disruption of the clans after the 1745 rebellion put an end to public observances in Gaeldom.

The Border country probably offers the richest variety of celebrations. In August in the ruins of Souden Church, under the massive sweep of the Cheviots, there is a public service commemorating the battle of Otterburn in 1388. The flag of the Red Douglas—a red heart on yellow cloth —is spread over the ruins of the chancel. The congregation sits on ancient gravestones. The Jedburgh town band plays music for the hymns and while the minister is preaching and praying clarinets and trumpets are laid in the summer grass.

The Red Douglas, who led the Scots, is said to have foreseen his own death in battle, and to have known that it would spur his army to victory.

> But I have dreamed a dreary dream
> Beyond the Isle of Skye:
> I saw a dead man win a fight:
> And I think that man was I.

At Arbroath there is a newly instituted commemoration of the famous Arbroath Declaration, the early statement of Scottish liberty which said in simple words, in 1320, that:

for so long as there shall be but one hundred of us remain alive we will never subject ourselves to the dominion of the English. For it is not glory, it is not riches, neither is it honour, but it is liberty alone that we fight and contend for, which no honest man will lose but with his life.

In July at Innerleithen, at the side of the Tweed, an effigy of the devil is cast into a bonfire during the ceremony of 'cleekin the de'il'. A form of football or handball was once played on feast days in most Border towns. It is still played in Jedburgh by the 'uppies' and the 'doonies'. The date of play is the Jedburgh equivalent of Shrove Tuesday (Fastern's E'en), a day which need not coincide with the ecclesiastical Shrove Tuesday. Jedburgh moves the movable feasts in its own way.

First come Candlemas, then the new mune,
The next Tuesday after is Fastern's Eve.

Jedburgh hand-ba' is a mass game and the ball is carried in tempestuous scrambles through houses and shops. The locked crowds of players sway through the streets past barricaded windows. It is free-for-all and all-in and the players are legion. The major, if not the only rule, and it is apparently unwritten, is that injuries should not be inflicted deliberately. Hand-ba' is one of the heartiest episodes in the Scottish year.

Throughout the land, during the summer months, many communities contribute to the living legend of their country. The ceremonies are all extremely popular and in some instances awaken deep feelings. They serve in the twentieth century, not as useless picturesque survivals, but to underline the sense of union between the Scotsman and his country.

*

I ground it in a quern on Friday
I baked it on a fan of sheep-skin
I toasted it to a fire of rowan,
And I shared it round my people.

I went sunways round my dwelling
In the name of the Mother Mary
Who promised to preserve me,
Who did preserve me,
And who will preserve me,
In peace, in flocks,
In righteousness of heart.

The Scottish year is quartered at Candlemas (February 2nd), Whitsun (May 15th), Lammas (August 1st), and Martinmas (November 11th). These are legal term days and arise out of the old Celtic and Teutonic year, variously divided into seasons, though some say the true division was not into four but into three, and others claim that there were only two major divisions, summer and winter.

The major festivals of the Celts were in May and November. Beltane or 'bright fire' was in spring and became stabilized on May Day. Samhain or 'summer end' led into the days of winter and is now the 31st of October or Hallowe'en. Beltane is still commemorated by name if not by belief. There is a Beltane Queen in Peebles and other towns. The celebrations that are now polite and decorative holidays probably included at one time animal or human sacrifices.

7

Though Samhain more or less approximates to Hallowe'en, portending the coming of the long nights, the old autumn fire festivals have been intermingled in other observances. Remnants of what used to be part of Samhain are found in Christmas and the New Year. The Yule Log is the vestige of the vast bonfires with which the Norse greeted the New Year.

The quarter days were important. They joined the natural seasons and one could not move from the deities of one season to the next without due caution. In Mull no one might borrow kindling from a neighbour because 'a kindling going out of a house on a quarter day takes along with it all the good luck'. A fire might be lit on the first day of a quarter to avert calamity, and occasionally first-footing was practised, a sociable custom now retained vigorously only at New Year. Quarter cakes were baked and people ate them in the open, throwing pieces over their shoulders to to propitiate wild animals: 'Here to thee, wolf, spare my sheep. There to thee, fox, spare my lambs. Here to thee, eagle, spare my goats.' On the first Monday of a quarter a living creature was thrust out of the house in the early morning, a sacrifice to the evil powers. But the first days of a quarter were lucky for new ventures. A very important point which people noted avidly was that on the first Monday of a quarter the smoke from a witch's house went against the wind.

Quarter days were also observed by the *Sith-Folk* or Good People. They

remove to other lodgings at the beginning of each quarter of the year, so travelling till Domesday ... Their chameleon-like bodies swim in the air near the earth with bag and baggage; and at such revolution of time, Seers, or men of the Second Sight (females being seldom so qualified) have very terrifying encounters with them, even on high ways.

In spring in Skye they used to catch a bumble bee.

We catch the first bum bee we see in spring and put it in our purse and we are sure not to be out of money till next spring.

On Islay a horse's ears were stuffed with butter on the first day of the ploughing season. In other parts of the Highlands, earth from the plough was rubbed on the horse's neck and shoulders. The harness, the plough and the horse's ears were sprinkled three times with water in which salt was dissolved. In Eriskay, salt water was sprinkled on the seed and on the sower. The seed was sometimes sprinkled with clear cold water three days before sowing in the name of the Father, the Son and the Spirit, while the sprinkler walked sunwise. A nail and an egg were placed beneath the seed in its basket. Or urine might be sprinkled on the cattle, from a broom dipped in bedroom slops. In the Borders it was believed that heather burned in spring helped to bring rain.

Summer was remarkably free of superstitious rites. The gods of fertility had already been propitiated. Winter was far ahead. There was work to do. Summer, leading to harvest, was the culmination of the year.

In autumn superstition was again used to invoke the protection of natural powers. The blooming of a white rose might mean an early death, a red rose an early marriage. When cattle were taken off pasture and housed for the winter, fire was carried round them three times, sunways. This practice was carried out till last century in the Hebrides.

The famous ring dance also survived into the last century. It was

the common dance at the *kirn* or feast of cutting down the grain, and was always danced with peculiar glee by the reapers at that farm where the harvest was first finished in any district. They danced to the music of the Lowland bagpipe; commencing the dance with three loud shouts of triumph, and thrice tossing up their hooks in the air. The intervals of labour during the harvest were often occupied by dancing the Ring, to the music of the piper who formerly attended the reapers.

In the old days the end of harvest was the signal for a festival of considerable heartiness, especially in the lusher Lowland regions. Flesh was eaten, often a rare occurrence for the crop-growing countryman, and long hours were given over to feasting and drinking and the lustration of pleasure. In the country the puritanical habits of the towns made less headway in subduing natural ardours. As recently as a generation ago farmers feasted their labourers after harvest. They employed gangs of Irishmen whom they supplied with straw, bannocks and beer as part of the fee. Up in the farm-house, when the job was done, belts were loosened and belches concealed while the farmer's wife plied everyone with abundance. The politest refusals were given when abundance had been sufficiently dealt with. 'Nae thank you, Maister Dobbie, I'm right fu''. 'I beg your pardon, Mistress, I could take no more.' Then back to the barn to doss, with a bottle of whisky for company, if not the dairy wench. In the towns the natural feasts have now dwindled to prim harvest festivals, as robust as barley water.

A winter observance in Lewis, early last century, was the

death revel when a man was elected king to reign from midnight till the cock crew.

A tub of cold water was poured over his head and down his throat, after which his face and neck were smeared with soot. When the man had been made as formidable and hideous as possible, a sword, scythe or sickle was placed in his hand as an emblem of office.

Death was turned into a mock king to be abused. The cold weather was a killer.

> *It kills sheep and lambs*
> *It kills the big kine one by one,*
> *And the horse at the same time.*

Christmas, now fully back into popular favour, was a favourite festival before the Reformation. On the rise of puritanism it was forbidden to observe the superstitious Popish Christmas. Those who were detected in the preparation of 'merriment' were summoned before a court. Many customs were transferred to New Year when they were regarded as being innocent and without superstition.

The reform of the calendar was repudiated in parts of the Highlands. New Year (Old Style) was observed for a long time in very many parts and there is still, in 1951, at least one small village that celebrates its New Year on January 12th. Last century, when bonfires were still lit at New Year, the hills around Inverness were crowned with flames on the 1st of January. To the north, across Cromarty Firth, the opposite hills were dark, but on the morning of the 12th they burst into flame.

Chapter Ten

FRED HOLME

TO LIVE OFF THE LAND

Here's tae ye a yer days,
Plenty meat an plenty claes;
Plenty parritch, and a horn spune,
And anither tattie when a's dune.

BELOW SELKIRK IS THE Haugh, the valley where the Ettrick flows. Across the river is an iron footbridge with a low railing.

One warm afternoon in early summer a boy, about fourteen years of age, stood near the centre of the bridge. He was fishing with a light rod and he had hooked a good-sized salmon which he played very skilfully. A small crowd of people gathered. By hooking the salmon the boy had become a poacher, member of a brotherhood that includes dignitaries of the Bench and the Church. Until he had the salmon landed and hidden away his enemies were the water

bailiffs, empowered to apprehend poachers, and any policeman who happened to come near. The small crowd was
friendly. It offered no advice, nor made any comment, but
the occasional smiles of individuals showed their appreciation of this piece of poaching in view of the town of Selkirk.
The sheriff court was one of the most prominent buildings
in sight.

When the boy had played the fish for some time, and it
was beginning to tire, an onlooker passed the word that the
bailiff was coming. This was a delicate dilemma. A nervous
fisher might have slipped the salmon or cut his line. The boy
let his rod droop so that the line hung loose. The tired
salmon sank to the bottom of the pool and rested, motion-
less and invisible. The boy leaned his elbows on the rail and
lounged with the dejected pose of a luckless fisher. The
bailiff crossed the bridge with heavy steps, not giving the boy
a glance. The knot of onlookers made disarming small talk
with each other, looked at the sky, yawned, and said 'Good-
day, Tom', to the bailiff.

When the bailiff disappeared in the distance the line was
reeled in and the boy played the fish as he moved from the
bridge to the shore. He netted the salmon and grassed it. It
was a clean-run fish of about twelve pounds. The boy un-
hooked it, lifted it with both hands and put it back in
the water. He had no use for it. Nor had anyone else.
Salmon was not a novelty for the table. The sport was the
thing.

At the head of a Border valley about ten miles from the
nearest town a farmer's wife keeps her larder well stocked
with poached salmon. She says with humour that the house
is so isolated she cannot have fish and chips unless she has

salmon. Her version is to grill the salmon steaks and serve the potatoes pounded with eggs and cream. She likes to get a few salmon at a time. They pickle well.

(To pickle salmon—cut in pieces, boil, and lay overnight on a dry cloth. Keep the liquor, and to one quart of it add two of vinegar, an ounce of black pepper, allspice and mace to taste. Boil the mixture and, when cool, pour over the pieces of salmon in a deep jar. Seal with a layer of edible oil and this will keep for a year.)

Scottish cooking is a pastoral cooking, brightly influenced by old ties with France. There is an old joke that if someone derides the French influence in Scottish cooking one asks them to translate the Scots phrase 'there's a gigot on the ashet'. A gigot is a leg of mutton. The ashet is the familiar *assiette*, reserved in Scotland to describe a large serving dish. Similarly, in a city tea-shop, it is quite correct to ask for petticoat-tails. This type of short-bread (*petits gastels*) is in itself an etymological lesson and a study in Scottish history.

The claret that was once used plentifully in the Scottish kitchen was not the equivalent of the fermented flavouring that some grocers sell as 'cooking sherry'. Claret was the national drink, far more so than whisky or beer. Wines were shipped to Scotland from Bordeaux and the Charente, and Leith imported many Mediterranean wines for the particular palates of the Scottish capital. There was a great to-do in the second half of the sixteenth century when a pint of claret increased in price twelve-fold over 50 years. As France was Catholic and Scotland effected its religious revolution during this period, one suspects a subtle manipulation behind the scenes to discredit the new régime. The wine trade was solidly for the Church of Rome. The Presbyters had to answer to the lieges about the fantastic cost of their favourite Popish wine.

The drinking of claret did not diminish till after the union with England. The need to find cash for England's wars made London governments, full of military bombast and indifferent to the civilized ways of the north, clap prodigious taxes on French wines, in favour of port from England's oldest ally. But old habits die hard and until the Hitler war many modest households kept a decanter of claret on the sideboard, and the visitor would be regaled with it instead of with tea or coffee. The custom is again growing.

In the early part of the eighteenth century, during the second half of Edinburgh's extraordinarily rich Golden Age, there was a zestful attitude towards good food. It was part of the intelligent romanticism of the Scott and Hogg entourage, and suggested a foreboding of the disastrous effect the industrial revolution would have on the national cuisine. A book with the homely title of *The Cook and Housewife's Manual* was published in Edinburgh in 1826. It came from the pen of Mistress Margaret Dods. Mistress Dods was reputedly the pen-name of the landlady of the Cleikum Inn in Peebles, a 'howff' frequented by men of letters. Mystery surrounds the volume. It is a disquisition on good eating as well as a compendium of dishes and the introductory pages were attributed by Blackwood's Magazine to Sir Walter Scott. But Blackwood's was probably in the secret. The book was certainly fathered by the authors of *Noctes Ambrosianae*. It is a gustatory monument to a period when learning 'in easy circumstances' made a virtuous marriage with good living.

The preamble includes ornate conversation pieces, larded well with rotund wit, poking fat fingers of fun in the ribs of the Church.

There comes a brother of the reformed order, whom I have never been able to teach the difference between Bechamel and buttermilk, though he understands ten languages . . . the Reformation has thrown the science of cookery three centuries back in this corner of the island. Popery and made dishes, eh, Mr Cargill?—Episcopacy, roast beef, and plum-pudding—and what is left to the Presbytery but its lang-kail, its brose, and mashlum bannocks?

Just before the Reformation a number of lean years made it necessary to legislate for austerity. In 1550 (about the time the price of claret began to rise) a parliamentary ordinance set up a form of rationing by aristocracy, providing that no archbishop, bishop or earl should have more than eight dishes at a meal. Lords, abbots, priors and deans were curtailed to six, barons and freeholders to four, and burgesses —men of substance—to three.

At once the other side of the medal is seen. The poor ate so miserably it was not necessary to control their meals. Porridge, kail, brose, barley-bannocks have carried thousands from infancy to a healthy old age. When there was not actual famine, the simple diet was sound enough. The baronial table groaned indecently, the fat burgesses belched, the Church had a proscriptive corner in the best arable lands, but the people of Scotland throve on cereals and milk and cheese. In diet as in other things, simplicity defends itself. When the tomato was known only as an exotic garden plant, long after Mistress Dod's Manual had found an honourable place in the library, children were warned not to touch the poisonous red fruit.

The student tradition of simple eating endures in the observance to-day of mid-term holidays in the Scottish Universities. The universities close on Meal Monday. The students used to take advantage of the long week-end to go home to replenish the meal sack that they carried to their city lodgings along with their books. Such rigorous scholarship earned an unnecessary jibe in the south when one of the more opulent and historic seats of provincial English learning accepted a Scots student with the remark that here was another to 'sleep in a garret, live on oatmeal and die on our hands'.

Some years ago in Italy I came upon a way of preparing porridge which made a neat comment on Scotland. The cook was a Chinaman who had mastered the southern European ways of cooking. I had acquired oatmeal and instructed the cook verbally in the preparation of porridge. He produced a most excellent plateful and served with it, as a natural thing to do with what was obviously the crude basis of a meal, a jug of pouring sauce, the full-bodied *sugo Bolognese* that goes rightly with spaghetti. So the poison fruit and the porridge were united in a way that underlined the simpler peasant economy of the north where no one had ever dreamed that porridge was anything but a complete dish in itself. I have to thank that Chinaman for his genius. By such hazards great recipes are discovered.

It is of passing interest that the northern way of eating porridge is to serve the milk (cream or buttermilk) in a separate dish. The spoon laden with porridge is then dipped in the milk. Pedantically to most, but as natural speech to many, porridge take a plural verb.

Scotland retains in its two largest cities a few eating-houses where traditional fare is understood. The ample intricacies of 'plain' and 'high' tea have fascinated and satisfied many visitors. The bakeries and tea-rooms of Princes Street and Sauchiehall Street provide teas that are a national festival of oat cakes, finnan haddies and *pâtisserie*.

Kail, brose and bannocks, sowens and sillocks, have an air of mystery to the foreigner (as well as to the contemporary city Scot). What is grown in the kailyard is cabbage (German—*Kohl*). With the potato it arrived late in Scotland. (Shetland did not acquire the cabbage until the eighteenth century.)

Bannocks are a small tribe, but the traditional barley bannock is made with barley-meal, butter, salt and sweet milk. The milk (with the butter and salt) is boiled and the barley meal stirred in to the thickness of dough. This is removed from the pot, rolled and cut into large rounds which are baked on a hot girdle, turned once, and eaten hot. A poke of barley meal was part of the baggage of a poor traveller. Lacking milk, he used water, and a hot stone was his girdle.

Simple brose is a form of oatmeal gruel, usually with butter added, though it can be titivated with honey, or wine. There are many brose soups, in which oatmeal is included in meat or shell-fish *potage*.

What one finds, on looking at Scotland's natural larder, is not the traditional monotony of oats and cabbage and potatoes, but a complex delightful cooking that made use of every edible scrap, from a lamprey to a bullock, from a nettle to a haunch of venison. If some of the dishes appear quaint to-day, it is our loss that we have been weaned away from them by foods that can be supplied in bulk for mass populations.

The poached salmon is cooked on the spot by poaching it, as one does an egg. Near the river a pot of water bubbles on a fire. As soon as the fish is landed it is cleaned and goes into the pot, which is taken off the fire at once and hidden in a bush. (The fire is extinguished so that the smoke does not betray the poacher.) When the water is cold the salmon is cooked. There is no better way of cooking it.

Partan bree (crab soup) made with rice and cream is one of the richer ways of gourmandizing. Crabs and lobsters are plentiful. Mussels can be bought in the High Street of Edinburgh from 'fish-wives' in traditional costume. They are supplied in a saucer and are eaten with a spoon at the pavement edge.

Because fishing is now carried out mostly on the deep sea, many of the delicacies of shore waters have been forgotten. At one time the Scots were civilized enough to relish the small octopus and squid that are found on rocky coasts. They may be stewed or fried, as happens in the Mediterranean. The flavour and texture of stewed octopus is delicious, like the tenderest veal tasting of oyster. The ink of the squid makes a sauce, unpleasant in appearance like muddy ink, but tartly excellent. Unfortunately, the Scottish recipes have vanished.

On the island of Colonsay there is—or was until very recently—a dish of limpet stovies. The limpets are boiled and removed from the shells. The juice is kept. The dish is made with alternate layers of shellfish and potatoes, not too highly seasoned. Add the juice and simmer for an hour under a cloth.

In those parts of the country where people still look for their food in the world around them the importance of seaweed has not been forgotten. Carrageen, dulse and sea-tangle have their own recipes. A milk soup can be made of sloke, and this seaweed can also be served 'solid' along with dulse, which is savoury, and potatoes added as a 'veg'. A seaweed meal, if one cared for such a thing, could be finished with carrageen which makes an excellent sweet with beaten egg and cream.

Nearly everything fresh can be preserved by pickling. The primitive way of preserving fish by drying and 'wind-blowing' is still carried on, as it is in Scandinavia. In some of the small islands it is still necessary to kill a cow when winter comes. The animal is put in a 'wet pickle' and lasts the season. (This is less alarming than in the Faroes where a 'dry pickle' is assisted by the cold atmosphere and a man knows he is approaching home on a dark night by the luminous glow in the outhouse.)

What an unsympathetic onlooker described as the belly-worship of Burns has raised the haggis to the status of a national dish. There are different kinds of haggis, but mainly mutton haggis or deer haggis. (There is also the four-winged bird of happy mythology which must be shot on the wing.)

The brutal preliminaries of haggis-making are not for the squeamish. The preparation of a haggis would be a test of a carnivore's faith. This is the recipe of Mistress Dods for a haggis that won the first prize in a haggis competition in Edinburgh.

Clean a sheep's pluck thoroughly. Make incisions in the heart and liver to allow the blood to flow out, and parboil the whole, letting the windpipe lie over the side of the pot to permit the discharge of impurities; the water may be changed after a few minutes' boiling for fresh water. A half-hour's boiling will be sufficient; but throw back half of the liver to boil till it will grate easily; take the heart, the half of the liver, and part of the lights, trimming away all skins and black-looking parts, and mince them together. Mince also a pound of good beef suet and four or more onions. Grate the other half of the liver. Have a dozen of small onions peeled and scalded in two waters to mix with this mince. Have some finely-ground oatmeal, toasted slowly before the fire for hours, till it is of a light brown colour and perfectly dry. Less than two teacupfuls of meal will do for this quantity of meat. Spread the mince on a board and strew the meal lightly over it, with a high seasoning of pepper, salt, and a little cayenne, first well mixed. Have a haggis bag (i.e. a sheep's paunch) perfectly clean, and see that there be no thin part in it, else your whole labour will be lost by its bursting. Some cooks use two bags, one as an outer case. Put in the meat with a half-pint of good beef gravy, or as much strong broth as will make it a very thick stew. Be careful not to fill the bag too full, but allow the meat room to swell; add the juice of a lemon or a little good vinegar; press out the air and sew up the bag, prick it with a large needle when it first swells in the pot to prevent bursting; let it boil slowly for three hours if large.

Meg Dods adds, 'this is genuine Scots haggis'. I have watched a Frenchman read these dainty instructions and say in dismay, 'I shall never understand the Scottish humour'. I reminded him that the French claim for their *hachis* the honour of originating the haggis. He shrugged and said politely that there were certain honours a country might be happy to relinquish.

There is a recipe for 'Het Pint' that should be preserved. This drink was once very popular, especially at New Year, when it was carried through the streets in a kettle. The tax on whisky has altered the nature of Scottish pleasures. Again the recipe comes from that most excellent woman, Mistress Meg Dods.

Grate a nutmeg into two quarts of mild ale, and bring it to the point of boiling. Mix a little cold ale with sugar necessary to sweeten this, and three eggs well beaten. Gradually mix the hot ale with the eggs, taking care that they do not curdle. Put in a half-pint of whisky, and bring it once more nearly to the boil and then briskly pour it from one vessel into another till it becomes smooth and light.

Of whisky little need be said except that malt whisky is best. 'Distillery' whisky drunk in a Highland inn (if one has not access to a distillery itself) is as different from most commercial whiskies as a vintage wine is from a rough *vin ordinaire*. There are only four ways in which a man may drink whisky if he is not to show himself a barbarian. It can be drunk neat; it can be taken with a little pure cold water; in cold weather it may be made into a hot toddy; and it can be served as Athole Brose.

The story behind Athole Brose is legendary. A boorish and powerful giant was annoying people in the neighbourhood of Athole in the Highlands. The chief offered the hand of his daughter in marriage to any man who killed the giant. Many tried and their mangled corpses were later found in the dark forests. The giant was formidable, but the daughter was beautiful. A young man who had been wisely instructed that brains might outmatch brawn made a study of the giant's habits from a distance. He discovered that the creature came every evening to drink at a hollow stone in a wood. The youth, whose ardour was combined with unusual maturity of taste, prepared a huge concoction of what is now known as Athole Brose. This he poured into the hollow stone. The giant, licking his lips, drank this in huge gulps, fell into a stupor and was promptly despatched. Some doubt has been thrown on the authenticity of this story by the suggestion that any man who had the secret of Athole Brose would not waste his time courting.

The drink has been a trap for lesser men than giants. Any who can buy or steal the ingredients will learn that 'whisky soup' is as near to nectar as one is like to get in an imperfect and mortal world. The preparation should be undertaken by the man of the house in the seclusion of his study. A silver spoon must be used. Athole Brose is the ceremonial drink of at least one Highland regiment.

Half a pound of fine oatmeal and half a pound of running heather honey are thoroughly mixed with a cupful of cold water. Two pints of whisky are *slowly* added to this. Stir briskly with the silver spoon till the mixture froths, then bottle and cork tightly. After a few days the corks may be reverently removed.

There is an intoxicating drink to be made from the sap of birch trees, but it takes five months to mature. For those whose thirst cannot endure such a period of trial, croppings of heather may be turned into a palatable ale. (It is also on record that green heather shoots may be used, suggesting a

8

spring brew as well as an autumn brew.) A large pot is filled with croppings which are covered with water and boiled for an hour. This is strained and the liquid is measured. For every twelve bottles add an ounce of ground ginger, half an ounce of hops, and one pound of golden syrup. Boil for twenty minutes and again strain, this time into a cask. When the brew is 'milk-warm' add a teacupful of barm or yeast. Covered with a cloth the cask should stand for a day and then be skimmed. The liquor is carefully poured into a tub so that the barm and sediment are left behind. Bottling and corking follow, and the ale is ready in two or three days. This is the famous Heather Ale, with a history going back to the time of the Picts.

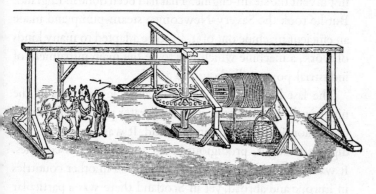

Chapter Eleven

TO CREATE, INVENT, DISCOVER

Here stand I at what is called the Cross of Edinburgh, and can in a few minutes take fifty men of genius by the hand.
—An eighteenth-century visitor.

THERE IS THE FAMOUS story of James Watt sitting by the kitchen fire and watching the kettle boil. If the steam moved the lid why should it not move—well, anything?

One might write at length on the type of curiosity that perseveres with such ideas. I have suggested in another chapter that there may be an explanation in the fusing of the twin attitudes of Highlander and Lowlander—the one with the imperial imagination, the restless impractical mind, the other with a painstaking observation of detail, a stubborn persistence. I fling that out as a fancy rather than a theory. But once the pattern of discovery and creation is set it seems a multitude of men will play their part in it.

One has to be extremely careful of the facts. Legend

already intrudes. James Watt, working from his kettle, did not invent the steam-engine. That had been done in England. But he took the Savery-Newcomen steam-pump and made an efficient machine out of it, fit to be adapted to many kinds of work, a machine which was to be the main instrument of industrial power till about the 1890's.

The last half of the eighteenth and the first half of the nineteenth centuries contained the greater portion of a period of extraordinary activity in Scotland. It was a period of prodigious thought, prodigious work, prodigious discoveries. It was integrated with what was going on in other countries in Europe and abroad, yet in Scotland there was a particular intensity, as though Scottish ways and methods and abilities were especially suited to the needs of the time. Very many of the technics of the modern world were fathered and nursed in this Golden Age of Scottish endeavour. Men of talent, with more than a sprinkling of men of genius, appeared in a diversity of fields—geology, astronomy, meteorology, natural history, medicine, surgery, in philosophy and mathematics, in the academic world, in workshops, and in back parlours where many ingenious devices were contrived.

Those who created were sustained by the belief that the miracle of mechanical power would solve the problems of mankind. They were unaware of the 'dark Satanic Mills' that were to rise after them; they had no idea that they were preparing the transformation of their country into desolate rural areas and mass metropolitan populations of hungry diseased multitudes.

Hopeful, eager energy was expended in all directions, and in all manner of activity—a special wheel, the principle of latent heat, discoveries about the circulation of the blood, a new outlook on the universe. Adam Smith wrote his *Wealth of Nations*. In philosophy Hume capsized the structure of thought that had been built over hundreds of years. He laid the foundation not only of subsequent philosophical thought but also of analytical psychology. Kant, who was stirred to write his *Critique of Pure Reason* in response, said that Hume 'woke him from his dogmatic slumbers'.

Looking back at the period, from mid-century to mid-century, one gets the impression of tumultuous activity. One is tempted to list a string of names as they come to mind, out of sequence, in no special order. The names, the discoveries, the years themselves, become mingled with steam and shale and coal and electricity, with anaesthetics, antiseptics, with poems and treatises and paintings. In the field of chemistry and physics alone there is a record of men that in itself demonstrates the progress of science—Black, Martine, Graham, Dewar, Playfair, Ramsay, Young, Beilby, Brewester, Swan, Clerk Maxwell, Lord Kelvin.

William Murdock who, like James Boswell, was born in Auchinleck, was the first man to light his home with coal gas. He did this in 1792. He also devised the first oscillating steam engine. Electricity—which by then was doing parlour tricks—followed in the next century. Clerk Maxwell ('Dafty' to his schoolboy friends) discovered the electro-magnetic field. At the age of fifteen he had sent a paper to the Royal Society of Edinburgh. In 1847 Professor Simpson discovered chloroform in Queen Street, Edinburgh, during a hilarious evening when his friends, willing experimenters, collapsed unconscious under his dining-room table.

James Nasmyth, member of a family that had a 'corner' in Scottish landscape painting, so many painters did it produce, invented the steam-hammer that bears his name. He had other inventions, and drew plans for a submersible ship in which the Admiralty showed no interest. A book of his had the fascinating title, *The Moon Considered as a Planet, a World, and a Satellite*.

The gigantic appetite for work and discovery was itself the most astonishing aspect of the age. Because the emphasis was technical and abstract, rather than artistic, the period has received less attention than it merits. What it produced has largely been accepted unthinkingly in our modern life. But though the fruits of the period were, eventually, telephones and wireless and modern surgery, and half a hundred other things, there was at the time an equal devotion to all aspects of life. Poets, theologians, philosophers, economists, surgeons, engineers, argued and talked and worked together. They were creating a new age, and were aware of it, just as they were aware of the background to their own brilliance —the filthiness and disease of the towns, the naked coalminers, men and women, spending most of the day underground, the poverty of the country workers, the bigoted narrowness of religion.

Professor James Hutton is probably the foremost example of a man creating a new science out of nothing but a tradition of uncompromising thinking. He was born in Edinburgh in 1726 and became the 'father of modern geology'. He was educated at the Royal High School in Edinburgh and then attended the Arts and Medical Faculties in Edinburgh University. Afterwards he went abroad. When he returned to Edinburgh he was more attracted by research in chemistry than by the practice of a medicine that was, in the 1740s, still crude and unattractive to his exploratory mind. He inherited a farm and after further travels he set himself up as a scientific farmer. His chemical knowledge was directed to the soil and through this he turned to the land and its formation. At that time it was accepted that God had created the world in six days. Attempts had been made to explain 'scientifically' the features of the earth, but only in terms that fitted with the Mosaic teaching of the Bible.

At the age of fifty-nine, in 1785, Hutton presented his paper *Theory of the Earth*, to the Royal Society of Edinburgh. To men who believed the age of the earth was exact and measurable in a few thousand years, he offered, with the neatness of an inductive argument, his ideas of the immensity of time and the true nature of the world. He showed the process of erosion and the building up of new land masses under the oceans. It was an intellectual *tour de force*. But then, so was Hume's *Treatise on Human Nature*, so was the *Wealth of Nations*. So indeed was Watt's steam-engine.

The theme of the arts was closely interwoven with the others. In painting there were, to say no more of them, the names of Alan Ramsay, David Wilkie, Raeburn, the Nasmyths.

Literary development began, possibly, with the elder Alan Ramsay who wrote *The Gentle Shepherd*, kept a wig-shop, and started the first circulating library. It moved through the poets, Robert Fergusson and Robert Burns. (Stevenson later said there had been 'three Roberts', Fergusson, Burns and himself.) It burgeoned most fulsomely into the romanticism of Scott and his coterie, the Ettrick Shepherd and Christopher North. It made Edinburgh share with Paris the twin honour of leading European literary centre. The impulse turned on itself, became critical, and produced the *Edinburgh Review* under the editorship of Francis Jeffrey. It was probably the most powerful single journal of criticism that Europe has ever known. Of the magazines which began in that period two survive to this day, *Blackwoods* and *Chambers*.

The invention of the steam-engine opened up new possibilities for commerce. The Scots had experimented with tramways before, and in due course it was a Scot who put the flange on wheels so that machine traction could be mounted on rails.

The tramways had a long history. The monks of Midlothian, who had hewn coal since the Middle Ages, had used crude trams to take the coal the short distance from the mines to the sea. (In 1745 General Cope had his battle lines at Prestonpans intersected by a tram-road or wagon-way. The rails were of wood and led from the Tranent coal pits to the harbour at Cockenzie. It is the wooden rails that give us the word: the Scandinavian *tram*, or *trum*, is a tree cut lengthwise into logs.)

About 1800 the Scottish engineer, Thomas Telford, became interested in tramways as an alternative to canals. He was the son of an Eskdale shepherd. He built canals in England, the Caledonian Canal, and the Gotha canal in Sweden. The major monument to his work is the suspension bridge over the Menai Strait between Anglesey and Wales.

He advocated the use of 'iron railways' in 'countries whose surfaces are rugged'. The horse was the locomotive power he proposed. Before the steam-engine was fitted to rails the

Lothians and the Tweed valley were surveyed for many railroad schemes, worked out in cost to the last penny, with estimated profits and percentage returns on capital.

It is for his roads that Telford is best known. Until the first half of the eighteenth century miserable road conditions had made trade almost impossible by land. In 1750 a journey between Edinburgh and Glasgow was 'an arduous undertaking at any season of the year. It could only be performed on foot or on horseback, and during the winter it was a matter of the utmost difficulty . . . not more than ten or a dozen carriages of any sort—carts included—passed in a year.' The distance was forty miles.

Telford did the civil engineering to transform the roads of Scotland and England—and Russia, too, for that matter— and Macadam invented a type of smooth durable surface. (Macadam was eventually appointed surveyor-general of metropolitan roads and granted £10,000.) Many years later, in 1887, Dunlop re-invented the pneumatic tyre. (It was a Scottish doctor who devised the way of impregnating cloth with rubber, an invention subsequently used by Mackintosh for his raincoats.)

Dunlop is an example of the great number of Scots who made discoveries in matters quite outside their normal business. He was a veterinary surgeon. When he died he was running a drapery business in Dublin.

Nasmyth, of the steam-hammer, was an example of the practical man produced by an artistic family, just as, in the contrary way, the Stevenson family of civil engineers and lighthouse builders, produced Robert Louis Stevenson. The balance between science and the arts was real, as though the Scots refused to have life arbitrarily divided into compartments. Life was to be seen whole, and the artist and the scientist were two aspects of the same person. (R. L. Stevenson's least-known work is, probably, his paper on *The Thermal Influences of Forests*. De Quincey, during his long residence in Edinburgh, must have been under the same dual influence when he wrote his *Logic of Political Economy*.)

Sir Walter Scott and his cronies may have turned an almost blind eye to technical development, but it was in an unconscious reaction to it that they re-explored the past and erected the New Romanticism which was to delight Europe, already excited by the 'Ossian' literature, the creation of another Scot.

The whole conception of modern shipping and ship-building was created when the stern-paddler, the *Charlotte Dundas*, built by Symington, was sent on her trials on the Forth and Clyde Canal, and then moved to Lochwinnoch because it was feared the canal banks would be damaged by that unparalleled occurrence, the wash of a steamship.

The welding of the practical technician and the imaginative artist into one team has its most enduring monument, perhaps, in the New Town of Edinburgh. The architect was a nephew of the poet James Thomson, a Scot best known as the author of *Rule Britannia*, though his *The Seasons* is a more meritorious claim to fame.

The New Town, planned and constructed by municipal enterprise, was built as an artistic and utilitarian unit, a combination to which we have now lost the key. That the citizens of Edinburgh should have decided to emerge, in an orderly Georgian way, from their ancient semi-medieval fortress city is an indication of the temper and mood of the time. Under crow-stepped gables and pepper-pot turrets they scrutinized not only the formal layout that is to-day a most valuable example of grace and elegance, but they handed over their plans to the master masons and the architects and decorators (men such as Playfair and the brothers Adam). The burgesses of Edinburgh, through their Town Council, refrained from interfering too much. They glimpsed perfection, instructed that it should be built, and paid the bill. (Under less careful management the town went bankrupt about 1830 and the New Town, by then far greater than in the original plan, was abruptly terminated.)

That this blossoming of talents could take place at all, in so many different ways, was due of course to the age providing many of the ideas and materials. It was also possible because Scotland was ready for it. Though the parliamentary union with England was a great set-back, almost a fatal *mésalliance*, there was a long heritage of European culture on which to draw. (Had not the religious philosopher Duns Scotus been the major antagonist of Thomas Aquinas?) Even in the bloodiest days of the fighting with England scholars were privileged persons permitted to pass freely from one country to the other. And the seas were the highways to Europe.

In the years of creation pious hopes swelled the breast of idealism. A professor of Natural Philosophy at Glasgow University (a man who helped James Watt) devoted part of his leisure to the invention of new weapons. He declared that

it is a pleasing reflection that the more the art of killing men in battle is improved, the fewer men are killed; as appears by comparing the lists of the killed and wounded in modern with that in ancient battles, when the numbers of combatants were equal.

During the feverish years when railways spread like a rash, the village poet, Andrew Scott of Bowden, wrote of the promise of plenty:

> And if th' rail-roads be determined there,
> Troth, you an me hae little cause to fear.
> May't be, as ye suppose, a happy land,
> That smiles a paradise on ilka hand.
> I think I see the clouds o' waggons come,
> Like travelling towns on wheels wi' coal an' lime,
> to fertilize and cheer our cauldrife clime.

In the middle of the eighteenth century the country was attuned for a great intellectual and technical revolution, offering a future full of the promise that a harsh and military past had denied. By the middle of the nineteenth century, the great age, as a national experience, was being clouded over by the gritty fog of industrialization. Other countries knew the same fog and were imprisoned in the service of the 'dark Satanic Mills'.

Though the full flowering was over by the 1850's the same type of comprehension and endeavour continued to show itself—in Hugh Miller, in Sir James Frazer, in Charles Doughty, Sir Arthur Keith, Lord Boyd Orr. It was Alexander Bell who invented the telephone; James Baird who invented television; Sir Alexander Fleming who discovered penicillin.

Is there something particularly Scottish in these Scotsmen, and in what they did? Take a group on whom the crown of genius sits not too uneasily—Hutton, Robert Burns, Adam Smith, Hume, Frazer. It is difficult to avoid the conclusion that their minds had one quality in common—a perception of 'universality'.

To analyse beyond that may be dangerous. Yet one must ask why this should be, consistently, generation after generation, the stamp of Scottish genius. The lesser men made their numerous discoveries. The giants were chasing the universe as a boy chases a ball. 'To hold infinity in the palm of a hand' is almost too easy a way of describing the attitude of mind which seeks the final shape of things through the traditional application to detail. It is a metaphysical attitude, and that may be its Scottishness. Scratch a Scotsman and you find a preacher. There was a necessity to work hard at the job on hand, to master the detail: this was a bred-in-the-bones austerity of purpose, the 'character' handed down from father to son in sour farms on windy hills. But specialization was shunned except as a path to a fuller understanding of the whole.

Something was derived—and here one treads warily—from Scottish Presbyterianism, or perhaps the Scottish Church was itself moulded by the same attitude but without the generosity and tolerance of genius. One is led through a religion which postulated a personal god (noting the intellectual pride and power of a people who denied any other person the right to stand between themselves and their divinity), to a metaphysical attitude of mind which penetrated the blind depths beyond knowledge and dogmatic faith.

Napier, who lived before this period, was a Scottish mystic who discovered logarithms. Hume was accused of atheism. Burns satirized the church and preached human values. The scientists amongst them came to irrefutable scientific conclusions—yet making few dogmas, always leaving the next page clear for direct controversion. The goal was never knowledge itself, nor even a limited understanding, but wisdom, an apprehension incorporating religion and philosophy and morality and the freedom of humanity. Whether the approach was by test-tube or by poetic stanza they were all travelling the same way.

Chapter Twelve

TO INHABIT CITIES

T HERE IS AN OLD belief that when a man dies away
from his own country his soul, as soon as it is released
from his body, speeds to his homeland by the most direct
route, even if it has to take the low road through the underworld. Death overcomes the barrier of distance for the
exile.

This explains the verses of one of Scotland's most famous
songs. A Scotsman, many years ago, was about to be hanged
beyond the frontier of the country. The reason for the hanging is unimportant. To his sweetheart, who was standing
near him, he sang a farewell song:

Ye'll tak the high road, and I'll tak the low road,
An I'll be in Scotland afore ye:
For me an' my true love will never meet again
On the bonny, bonny banks of Loch Lomond.

It is a pleasant mythological fancy to picture the spirits of dead Scots hurrying across the continents and seas of the world to their native glens and mountains, each seeking the rural charm of his childhood days. It is unsettling to recall that the greater number of Scots—the stout peasant race of the north—are born and bred amid the stone and lime of the cities. The great industrial belt that straddles the centre of Scotland and reaches a tentacle through Fife to Dundee, contains far more than half of the Scottish population.

The bonnet lairds of the past, the Highland crofters, the island fishers, the Lowland farmers, have bred families who are mechanics and civil servants and warehousemen and insurance agents. Scotland, so long regarded as a country of rugged and rural solitude, is, for most of its people, a narrow sunless city street with a pub at one end, a co-op at the other, and a grey smoky sky overhead.

It is not so long since Edinburgh was the only city of consequence in Scotland. The ancient capital is now at one extreme of a proliferous industrial sea. It is surrounded by dockyards and coalfields. The commercial capital, Glasgow, is at the other extreme. The forty or so miles between is a gigantic midden of furnaces and slag-heaps, of pits and mines and refineries, of factories and marshalling yards. A pair of dungarees, an old oily battle-dress tunic, a miner's safety helmet, are the national garb of Scots far more than the kilt and the bonnet.

Glasgow is the hub, the driving force of this exceptional

industrial activity which supplies, when times are good, the wage-packets of the majority of Scots. When times are bad, hunger stalks the streets of the cities just as famine used to stalk the Highland glens.

The Glasgow man is the first to admit that the only reason for living there is to earn a living. There are none of the graces of life within its boundaries, and few of the ordinary joys. But inside the dour metropolis a human quality persists, giving Glasgow a personality, an atmosphere, that is not known in other cities of comparable magnitude and function.

It has been seen in small things. In Glasgow a tram conductor is likely to offer a cigarette if he sees you gazing mournfully at an empty packet. An urchin, of whom you ask the way, will accompany you to your destination, out of an illiterate gutter courtesy, full of the chatter of a street sparrow, with no obvious speculation on a reward.

Glasgow remains indescribable. There is no disparagement in this admission. Language is not enough to describe this pullulating city, a Moloch that makes a daily meal of coal and steel and men and women. Yet there is so much more to Glasgow. It is efficient, certainly, in a crude wasteful way, but it does not fit into the industrial order of cities, like Sheffield or Pittsburg. 'Douce, raucle citie' it was called by the poet, John Kincaid. 'Our black, fierce city,' said Walter Elliot. Human qualities, it will be noted, and the poet saw the tenderness behind the iron façade.

The point of Glasgow is that so much squalor, so much prostrating before the terrible gods of industry and commerce, has bred a new kind of courtesy. It is the obverse to the kindliness that is found amongst people in the depths of

9

the country. It is a defence, a last protection of flesh and blood against the implacable hostility of poverty and disease and the hard menace of steel and stone.

The rest of Europe is fortunate, in mid-twentieth century, in having no slums comparable to those of Scotland. In magnitude the foul dead-centre of Glasgow is greater than anything in Edinburgh or Dundee. Here generations have rotted, individuals have lost the identities that were of no value to them and have become whisky-soaked derelicts, or they have made their sub-human protests against society with the dagger edges of broken bottles and the slash of razors. Here, too, with Messianic prophecies, were men like Keir Hardie and John Maclean, building out of the degradation of the human spirit a political machine that fathered the major social changes of this century. But the rest of the country has benefited more than the inner heart of Glasgow where the legions of the lost still live in their city of dreadful night.

All the long story of human agony and endeavour is contained in the short life of Glasgow, and in its humanity. To be human is a condition, and one dare not make too much of it. It is warm-blooded; it may also be scruffy, resigned, backward and stupid. It may be a state of crucifixion.

Glasgow's few ancient buildings and connections are forgotten in the insistence of growth and expansion and struggle. It is entirely a modern city. The giant derricks along its waterfronts, the desolate miles of warehouses, the iron gates to hundreds of factories, the outrageously opportune brick edifices—flung up cheaply and quickly so that there was not time to build with blocks of Scottish masonry—the sense of purpose behind the raucous effort, the way the city reaches into the deep water channels to the west, and east-wards to the iron furnaces and the bings—all these things incessantly interact to show its real function as a machine of production, where all the citizens are mechanics tending its multifarious needs. Glasgow has the dedicated purpose of a machine, and the noise and the stench and the dirt and the slums are the waste products of its lustful energy. Its life is linked with the roar of a Bessemer retort, with the thunder of a coal chute, with the sense-numbing hammer of pneu-matic riveters, with the hiss of the tyres of heavy lorries on asphalted highways.

But stand on a bridge over the Clyde in the flaring red light of an autumn sunset. The derricks dig their articulated knuckles into apricot clouds. Beyond the roof-tops, beyond the sea-going ships and the 'puffers' and the barges, are—somewhere through the smoke—the nearer hills of the High-lands. The country comes to Glasgow's door. One senses it in the winds that blow from the west, lifting the paper scraps in the streets, ruffling the Clyde, making the pedestrians huddle within their coat collars. Loch Lomond is not thirty miles away, and the bonny, bonny banks contain the effluent of a hydro-electric scheme. In summer the citizens make their pilgrimages there, the bourgeois well-to-do in their cars that make a tour of hostelries in the social round of whiskies-and-sodas and gins-and-its, the more vital citizens on their bicycles with their blackened billy-cans bouncing on the carrier-bags. But locked in the inner keep of Glasgow's poverty are citizens who have never seen a field or a tree on a hill-side, to whom the thirty-mile journey to Loch Lomond is as familiar as a trip to the moon.

Yet Glasgow, as well as being astonishingly ugly, as well

as recording in its gaunt growth the economic and social history of last century and this—Glasgow is fortified with glamorous spectacle. At night it has a peculiar vigour. The streets that traverse and bound its central quadrangles of offices become broad and endless at night, when electric lights shine on empty spaces and the night population moves mysteriously on its secret business. Cabs and coffee-stalls, men with barrows, solitary cars snoring up the steeper streets, stray patrol cars rounding corners like sensitive watch-dogs, are wrapped in the atmosphere of a city at night, with the gleaming wetness of newly washed roads, the blank inscrutable windows, the jar of a phrase of music as a door opens, the uncomfortable loudness of normal talk in the sounding box of a city square, the menace of a great building locked behind the strength of barred doors and grilled windows, the helpful human advice of the vendor of a sausage roll: 'I wouldny go down that street, mister, there's trouble with some of the boys there. If you don't want to take a taxi then cut up by Argyll-street and you'll be all right.'

The poet John Kincaid, in *A Glesca Rhapsodie*, writes:

> *Eh, ma citie o raucle sang,*
> *ma braid stane citie wi dwaums o steel.*
> *Eh, ma Glesca, ma mither o revolt,*
> *dauran the wunds o time in a raggit shawl.*
> *Eh, ma hanselt hinnie wi scaurs o war,*
> *ma twalmonth lassock, ma carlin ages auld.*

The other answer to the tyranny is to hit the bottle till the stars settle in Sauchiehall Street: 'When Ah get drunk on a Setterday night, Glesca belongs tae me!'

Glasgow, strong, avaricious, tyrannous, full of wayward human feelings, makes poets or drunkards of those who do not succumb.

It is customary to compare Glasgow with Edinburgh, to make comments about the obvious disparities between the two cities. It is the two together that make the urban heart of Scotland. They complement rather than contradict each other. What has been called the coldness and reserve of Edinburgh is real enough in contrast with the warm humanity of Glasgow. But Edinburgh is not of this age. It is a composite city, built of the Scottish past. It has been called 'history in stone': it has also been variously recorded as a 'dirty, stinking town' and 'the Athens of the north', a fair indication of the responses it can awaken.

Edinburgh is a cemetery of the centuries. It remains a capital by the grace and favour of history, a principal city with no parliament or court, no ministers of state, no representatives of foreign powers. It is like a prima donna, long retired from the opera-house, without a role to play or the ghost of a song to sing. In spite of its appearance of a bustling centre of commerce and trade Edinburgh—as the capital of Scotland—is a gesture to the past. It is the tenuous, persistent, pervasive evocation of the past that gives the solid stone of the city its fragile charm, so that even the dour hugeness of the castle—which dominates central Edinburgh as the Alps dominate Interlaken—contains a reflective delicacy. The canty winds, that snuffle and run up the wynds and closes of Old Edinburgh, rattle windows and doors and stir the tears of things. Edinburgh is a paradise for the romantic historian; the past populations are safely out of the way; the rosy imagination sees history in its own light. The Gothic crown of lovely grey stone that rests on the tower of the Cathedral Church of St Giles is almost too fitting a symbol of antiquity. One can select the appropriate detail to suit the particular mood—the shadowed view down a close, the texture of a wall, the legend of a building. It is an insidious delightful trickery that Edinburgh offers.

Looking at the larger patterns of the city it is less easy to be mesmerized. The High Street (somewhat inappropriately called the Royal Mile, for there is little of the exclusiveness of royalty in its warm impoverished humanity) is a hodge-podge of old and recent, of seventeenth-century corbels and pepper-pot turrets, of painted beams and scenic ceilings, of chromium emporiums for cheap furniture, of the predatory establishments of curio-mongers on the watch for tourists, of the pathetic eloquent shabbiness of old clothes shops. The High Street has less of a consistent nuance of atmosphere than a hundred blunt indications of ancient and modern—a shed for sedan-chairs, a vast parliament hall that has not known a parliament for two hundred and fifty years, ruinous turnpike stairs up which children go from council schools to eat their fish-and-chip suppers in insanitary rooms that have a guide-book bloom of romance on them because they once housed—in an even less sanitary way—a pedigreed aristocracy. There are narrow closes leading to muddy court-yards that still show the raddled defaced dignity of a better-to-do prime. There are buildings for municipal administration, hock-shops, a satisfying number of pubs, police cells and waste spaces. There is also an intrusion of industry which brings into this tatterdemalion region a grimy efficiency like the self-satisfied belch of a self-made man who has made a deal over a heavy lunch.

What glamour there is in the ugliness of Glasgow is honest, a matter of steel and smoke and noise making a comment on contemporary man. The glamour of the High Street of Edinburgh is, correctly, history in stone, history with its agony and its dullness washed away, and in its place the excitement of sentimental excess.

Who live in the High Street? Who lean out of the high windows above the plunging buses and hang their washing against the sky on those extraordinary contrivances of wood and cord which jut from the walls and were invented for drying clothes seven stories up when there was no garden at the back of the house? There are few to match the story of the High Street, except in the theme of poverty. Edinburgh is unlike Glasgow where everyone plays his natural part as a citizen-mechanic tending a metropolitan machine. There are few natural roles left in Old Edinburgh. A poet, an artist or two, live in the High Street, and touch the scabrous plaster of their abodes like pilgrims touching the effigy of a saint. But they, though they understand the High Street, are not of it. They are intelligent sensitive in-dwellers. The true denizens are the families who are descended from the families who have always lived there. There cannot be many. Their ancestors were eighteenth-century 'caddies', seventeenth-century link-men, sixteenth-century water-carriers, fifteenth-century pike-men. Their children play at 'bools' and 'hop-scotch' in the gutters and on the pavements. In their speech they preserve, much adulterated, the Scottish 'lallans' tongue that was once spoken throughout Edinburgh. In their small crowded rooms, which most of them would change readily for a new 'cooncil hoose' or a prefab, they roost unconsciously on the ruins of their nation.

Down from the vertiginous walls of the old 'lands' and tenements, across the railways and flower-beds and tram-lines of the Princes Street valley, is the New Town—as prosperous and complacent as the Old Town is poor and unquiet. When it was designed and built at the end of the eighteenth century the New Town was an harmonious tribute to an age of taste and elegance. It has since then been severely punished by the successful commercial and financial life of the city. Its complex simplicity has been mutilated by ornate banks and provocative insurance buildings. The New Town was planned for residences and those northern streets and 'circuses' which have continued in the bespoke role have preserved a Georgian neo-classic beauty that time has mellowed and strengthened. The citizens of the New Town have been more civilized in their domestic life than in their business undertakings.

Though the essential Edinburgh is the Old Town and the New Town, and the incomparable balance of effects that they make in juxtaposition, it is always too easy to be misled by attention to detail—to praise this and decry that—suggest-ing that Edinburgh is only the sum of its parts. One can well ignore the new suburbs, the vast hinterlands of bungalows and semi-detacheds and harled blocks of flats. Central Edin-burgh remains a masterpiece, battered, misused, but a work of art, to be approached for its total effect rather than its miscellaneous attributes. So much has gone to the making of this masterpiece, both visible and invisible. A sense of time, for example, which to some is as evocative as a per-fume, clings to the city like a transparent varnish heighten-ing its tones and harmonies. The one o'clock gun, which bangs brusquely from the half-moon battery in the castle, is more startling in Edinburgh than it would be elsewhere. It is a recall from the insubstantial time-sequence of the sensile atmosphere, where all centuries are one, to the incommoding precision of the exact contemporary minute.

Of the miscellaneous attributes there is the delightful Parthenon on Calton Hill, as unexpected as a nymph at a Gothic festival; there is the view of Arthur's Seat that one gets from Princes Street, across the graceful arches of the North Bridge. There is the mist of green in spring-time in Princes Street gardens, so that the black solid base of the castle rock is verdantly washed with colour; there are the dense mists that annihilate surroundings, when the sound of ships' sirens and horns drone into the centre of a city that might be Manhattan in a fog; there are unexpected views, angles, points of observation, so varied and changing that even an elderly inhabitant during a morning stroll can come on one he has not seen before and feel that he is a stranger enchanted by his city for the first time.

Scottish cities, as well as their workaday appearance, have a Sabbath garb. The Scots Sabbath was made for man, deliberately, like a hair-shirt or a nagging wife. This does not matter so much in the country where there are natural diversions. In the cities it is like the line of James Flecker, 'all that calm Sunday that goes on and on'. Especially in Edinburgh, in the grey light of a Sabbath day, there is neither vice or virtue but a compromise between God and the Devil in which life yawns and accomplishes nothing. The young Scots take to their mountains.

Chapter Thirteen

TO SPEAK WELL OF THE HIGHLANDS

Còmhlan bheanntan, stòiteachd bheanntan,
còrr-lios bheanntan fàsmhor,
cruinneachdadh mhullaichean, thulaichean, shléibhtean,
tighinn 's a' bheucaich ghàbhaidh.

—Sorley Maclean.

(A company of mountains, an upthrust of mountains, a
great garth of growing mountains: a gathering of summits,
of knolls, of hills coming on with a fearsome roar.)

MORAYSHIRE, OR THE LAICH of Moray as it is called,
lies outside the Highlands. Its fertile fields and warm
woods are between the Grampians and the sea. The Romans
called it the granary of Scotland. The men of Moray, secure
in the comfort of their rich land, have always regarded the
Gaelic Highlanders as people with whom it paid to be civil

but not over-familiar; 'Speak well of the Highlands, but live in the Laich.'

How wise the men of the Laich have been. Their little towns have prospered down the centuries. When there was hardly a passable road in the rest of Scotland the men of Moray were sending their beef and tallow, their hides and malt, to France and in return they got 'wine, brandy, soapp, powder, reasins, ffigs, prunes, green ginger, suggar, pepper, indigo, cloves, nutmegs, rice, needles, muslen, camels' hair, mourning creapp, hatts of the newest fashion (all black), white Rhenish wine, tobacco, pypes, Ffrench wines'.

The Abbey of Pluscarden exercised a benevolent authority over the people. An occasional royal frenzy disturbed the peace of the lieges. Macbeth has a royal residence at Forres. An outburst of medieval pyromania destroyed the cathedral at Elgin. But on the whole, on the long average of the centuries, the men of Moray prospered.

As the stormy mountains contrasted with the flat Laich so did the Highlander compare with the men of Moray. The Highlander was different: he was different from all the men of the south, Scots or English. He spoke a different language, his songs and traditions were different. Those differences in time made it necessary to exterminate him. In a way it was fitting that the military defeat of the Highlander should have taken place on a bleak moor at the western end of the Laich—half-way between the Lowlands and the Highlands.

George of Hanover, on the British throne, was anxious to settle the 'Highland question'. Britain could not turn to its growing affairs abroad as long as this large northern society of different language and doubtful loyalty was entrenched in its glens and bens. The destruction of the Highlander was an obvious move of sound state-craft. It began with redcoat expeditions establishing their forward garrisons at Fort George, Fort William and so on. When the ambitious and not very competent Bonnie Prince Charlie arrived he served as excuse to set off an explosion that was already primed. The rout of Prince Charlie and the Highlanders at Culloden was the beginning of the end. It also ended King George's worry over a Stuart rebellion.

That only a limited number of Highland clans had supported the rebellious Prince was no reason to lessen the effort to end the Highland problem. The clan system was destroyed. All that was Gaelic suffered. Even the manuscript books of the Gaels, precious volumes of Celtic literature, were burned in bonfires by the redcoats. The legend of the 'savage Highlander' was created. It was no longer necessary to speak well of the Highlands.

The so-called Black Act prohibited the wearing of Highland dress. The penalty was six months' imprisonment for a first offence, and seven years' transportation for a second. An oath, destroying Highland custom, was drawn up in these words: 'I,......, do swear as I shall answer to God at the great day of judgement, I have not, nor shall have in my possession, any gun, sword, pistol, or arm whatever, and never use tartan, plaid, or any part of the Highland garb; and if I do, may I be cursed in my undertakings, family, property, may I never see my wife and children, father, mother, or relations, may I be killed in battle as a coward, and lie without Christian burial in a strange land, far from the graves of my forefathers and my kindred; may all this come across me if I break my oath.'

Once the clan system was broken and many of the old chiefs had been either killed or brought to heel, the British Army found that the Highlander made a good warrior. It took some time to accept him. The question of loyalty exercised the War Office. General Wolfe had occasion to write:

I should imagine that Highlanders might be of use. They are hardy, intrepid, accustomed to a rough country, and no great mischief if they fall. How can you better employ a secret enemy than by making his end conducive to the common good? If this sentiment should take wind what an execrable and bloody being I should be considered!

The myth of the savage Highlander was translated into the fact of the Highland soldier. Through the Seven Years War, the wars of Napoleon, the Crimean War, in Europe, Asia, Africa, America and India the Highlander fought for his Empire. Against the Kaiser, against Hitler, and in Korea, he was accustomed to bear his full share of the front line. Over this long period Highland losses in actions have been greater, on the basis of population, than those elsewhere in Britain. (I remember a Highland sergeant-major in Tunis chuckling over a newspaper: 'You'll see here how the English army chased Rommel from Egypt, across Libya, into Tunisia. D'you remember what the English army was?—a division of Jocks and a division of New Zealanders, they're the only infantry who went all the way. And, begod, I think half the New Zealanders were Jocks.')

The Highlander's troubles were not at an end when he accepted the golden guinea. If he left home he was probably killed. If he stayed at home he was possibly evicted. The mass evictions of Highland communities continued into the second half of last century. Those were the 'clearances' by which unsympathetic landlords, answerable to nothing but their own authority, cleared the land of its people in order to raise sheep on a large and profitable scale. Villages were burned. In the night the gorse burned red. Men and women and children were driven into the snow by bailiffs whose major weapon was a legal warrant. It was then that vast emigrations took place to Newfoundland and Canada and to other parts of the world, so that the Gaelic language is to-day spoken as a natural tongue on the other side of the Atlantic.

There is a verse in the anonymous Canadian Boat Song:

> When the bold kindred, in the time long vanished,
> Conquered the soil and fortified the keep,—
> No seer foretold the children would be banished
> That a degenerate lord might boast his sheep.

The last links with this policy of destruction are almost severed. After the Second World War a woman died in Skye: she was very old and she remembered seeing, when she was a child, a village put to the flames to oust the inhabitants.

The cause of the original 'clearances'—the speculative raising of sheep as a more paying concern than humans—was abortive. Australia produced sheep at a much keener price. The empty lands were turned into sporting estates. Deer and grouse occupied the desolate acres.

After two centuries the wheel is turning again. The future, with its hydro-electric schemes, its tweed marketing, and so on, may develop a new picture. But, in the middle of the twentieth century, the Highlander is not yet living in a new modern age so much as at the tail-end of two centuries of suppression.

A visitor gets the impression not of a community and a people (such as is presented in the roughly equivalent mountains and valleys of Switzerland or Norway) but of a number of isolated groups with little in common, fragments of the past that have somehow survived. Beside a small island with a village of fishermen there is another island with nothing but ruined houses. A village in one glen is busy and prosperous because it is the centre for a hinterland of valleys. Twenty miles away is another village where the last family left two years ago and many of the houses are still wind and weatherproof for any who care to enter. The land in one valley is well tilled and new houses have been built in the last twenty years, with a high-road and electricity. Over the hill, in a parallel valley, there is ground crying for the plough and the ruins of old houses rise above the grass.

The 'clearances' must be understood if the Highlands are to be understood, if one is to appreciate the humble pride, the apparent fatalism, the warm humanity that seem to be buried unusually deeply below the modern Highlander's 'san fairy ann' acceptance of life. The past lingers in the present just as yesterday's storm litters to-day's streets with debris. North of the Highland line the past is not very far away. There were actions in court, in 1951, to prevent Highlanders tilling their native soil. Not all the power of the welfare state nor the authority of government can persuade backward landlords to put their land under cultivation for the benefit of the Highland people.

There are hundreds of square miles kept deliberately barren of crops and houses, where, in the words of T. S. Eliot, 'the patient stag breeds for the rifle'. But, in the words of the same poet who showed a quick and intuitive understanding of the Highlands, 'memory is strong behind the bone'.

The Reverend Donald Sage had a ministry in Sutherland during the clearance that has been held as the most notorious and wanton. He wrote that 'the Sutherland clearance in 1819 was not only the climax of their system of oppression for many years before, but the extinction of the last remnant of the ancient Highland peasantry in the north'. When the eviction orders were served it was ordained that they were all 'man, woman and child—from the heights of Farr to the mouth of the Naver, on one day, to quit their tenements and go—many of them knew not whither'.

The minister held his farewell service to his people in Langdale in Strathnaver. It was an unusually fine morning. The country was looking its best for those who were being driven away for ever.

The service began. The very aspect of the congregation was of itself a sermon, and a most impressive one. Old Achoul sat right opposite to me. As my eye fell upon his venerable countenance, bearing the impress of eighty-seven winters, I was deeply affected, and could scarcely articulate the psalm. I preached and the people listened, but every sentence uttered and heard was in opposition to the tide of our natural feelings, which, setting in against us, mounted at every step of our progress higher and higher. At last all restraints were compelled to give way. The preacher ceased to speak, the people to listen. All lifted up their voices and wept, mingling their tears together. It was indeed the place of parting, and the hour. The greater number parted never again to behold each other in the land of the living.

The same minister described the appearance, years later, of that region.

The townships in every strath and glen, and on every hill, which once teemed with life, are now desolate and silent;

and the only traces visible of the vanished, happy population are, here and there, a half-buried hearthstone or a moss-grown graveyard.

This particular mass eviction is still talked of in the Highlands as a topic of interest. The ducal family responsible for it had, years later, the occasion to approach such tenants as were left on its estates in the hope of raising volunteers to fight in the Crimean wars. The Highlander, dispossessed or not, was still a fit man to die in the wars.

In his *Gloomy Memories of the Highlands* Donald M'Leod has left an account of a meeting when four hundred men gathered to hear the duke ask for soldiers to enlist in the 93rd Highlanders where they would redound to his own credit. He offered a bounty of £6 over and above the government bounty. When he had addressed the men he asked those volunteering to step to the table at which he and his factor were sitting, and where the money was spread. Not a man in the audience moved, nor was any remark made. The duke asked the cause of their 'non-attention'. There was still no response. The audience was utterly quiet.

At last an old man, leaning upon his staff, was observed moving towards the Duke, and when he approached near enough, he addressed his Grace something like as follows: 'I am sorry for the response your Grace's proposals are meeting here to-day, so near the spot where your maternal grandmother, by giving forty-eight hours notice, marshalled fifteen hundred men, to pick out the nine hundred she required, but there is a cause for it, and a grievous cause, and as your Grace demands to know it I must tell you, as I see none else are inclined in the assembly to do it . . . these lands are devoted now to rear dumb brute animals which your parents considered of far more value than men. I do assure your Grace that it is the prevailing opinion of this country, that should the Czar of Russia take possession of Dunrobin Castle and of Stafford House next term, that we could not expect worse treatment at his hands than we have experienced at the hands of your family for the last fifty years. Your parents, yourself, and your commissioners, have desolated the glens and the straths of Sutherland, where you should find hundreds, yea, thousands of men to meet and respond cheerfully to your call, had your parents and yourself kept faith with them. How could your Grace expect to find men where they *are not*, and the few of them which are to be found among the rubbish or ruins of the country, have more sense than to be decoyed by chaff to the field of slaughter, but one comfort you have, though you cannot find men to fight, you can supply those who will fight with plenty of mutton, beef, and venison.'

The memory of these events lives to-day—'strong behind the bone'—and is bitter to the Highlander. It was the Scottish poet, Hamish Henderson, who said in the foreword to his recent book, *Elegies for the Dead in Cyrenaica* (written about the war in North Africa where the Highland Division fought), 'I was thinking especially of the Highland soldiers, conscripts of a fast vanishing race, on whom the dreadful memory of the clearances rests and for whom there is little left to sustain them in the high places of the field but the heroic tradition of valour.'

The Highlands have been scoured by a great tragedy. Robert Louis Stevenson saw the Highland story in its sombre elemental simplicity:

> Lo! for there, among the flowers and grasses,
> Only the mightier movement sounds and passes;
> Only winds and rivers,
> Life and death.

Chapter Fourteen

TO PASS THE TIME OF DAY

For if the Highlanders have been undeservedly criticized, they have also been undeservedly praised, and in fact the controversy over their merits and faults has often been waged in an atmosphere of complete unreality.

—Hugh MacDiarmid.

I HAD TAKEN SHELTER in an abandoned roadmen's hut in a small quarry off a road in north-west Ross. There was no house within miles. At two in the morning a storm broke and some time later I saw what appeared to be a small man trying to open the window. He was held in black outline by a lightning flash. Fear and relief passed in a second. He was entirely human which, considering the isolation and the history of the region, appeared to be quite fortunate.

The stove blazed in a short time and he dried himself. He was a merchant navy officer and was spending his leave fulfilling a long-standing ambition, to walk round Scotland and have a drink in every pub.

'This is the second day that I haven't even seen a pub.'

'On some of the roads you're lucky if you see a house in a day's walk.'

'Oh, there were houses enough. Half a dozen crofts, a farm or two, and a post-office in a small cottage that looked out to acres of empty moor in front and the empty sea behind. What a country!'

'You sound impressed.'

'Too true. When you're cooped in a ship and can't walk ten feet without turning a corner and bumping into someone then you appreciate this kind of country. I was brought up in a city but I like space—space!' As he said it he flung his arms wide and cracked his knuckles on the stove chimney.

A man goes to the Highlands for many reasons. His guide-book is cluttered with the trivial nonsense that has become enshrined in tourist publications—fairy flags, sites of massacres, legends of green men, and dark men, and small men, Loch Ness Monsters and seal-women. If he stays south of the Great Glen he is looking for relaxation in pleasant and unusual country. If he goes north of the Great Glen he is looking for solitude and 'space', so much space, immense, inviolate, unpeopled, wild, that it is frightening and humbling.

What a man takes away from the Highlands is probably not a coherent picture of a region. He is mostly uninterested in its historical outline beyond what the guide-book tells.

He is not concerned whether the Highlander was a 'noble savage' or a traduced 'civilizer'. What he will remember are the human incidents, the isolated meetings with an old woman who did not understand English, or a man who made paper flowers to sell for drink and never travelled beyond the county boundary.

In the Highlands a meeting, a conversation, a hospitable dram or a cup of tea, have remained social occasions. They are more important than tag-ends of knowledge about the antiquity of the Celts and the ancient Gaelic culture. When such things are mentioned someone is sure to make the indisputable remark that knives and forks reached the Hebrides only last century, and that there are people alive who remember when dinner-time meant that two pots were emptied on the earth floor of the room—a pot of potatoes and a pot of herring. The family got down on its knees and grabbed with its fingers, and if it was a fastidious family the hens were put outside. Someone else will remark about the poetry of Duncan Ban MacIntyre or Iain Lom, or mention the enlightened phase in the Dark Ages when the Celts in Ireland had the brightest civilization in Europe.

'Barbarians', says one. 'Displaced civilizers', says another. It is difficult to make comprehensive conclusions.

Hamish, of course, was a fraud. His 'black house' was near a town where hundreds of tourists go every year. Hamish took advantage of this. I heard about him in the local pub. I had walked quite near to his house, across a moor, before I realized that I had arrived. The squat mound was like something that had grown from the ground.

When I was fifty yards away a gnomish figure leaped from

behind a bush and scuttled to the building. The door was pulled to and a key turned. As I watched, trickles of smoke began to seep through the thatch.

The house was lozenge-shaped, very squat and with walls that sloped inwards. The thatch was old and weatherworn. The place was neglected and dirty like an isolated slum. The door showed its constituent planks. It was set in a small gap in the stonework which was black with age and growing thickly with weeds. The ground was an ooze of mud and cow pats.

I knocked. A thin voice answered at once: 'Yes, please?' There was only the door between us.

'May I come in?'

There was a sound of asthmatic breathing. Then the door was unlocked and a chain rattled, Hamish smiled up at me. 'Please come in. I've just lit the fire.'

He was not a small man but he was bent almost double with rheumatism. His hair hung in clotted tufts and his dirty dark skin creased and wrinkled when he smiled. His smile had a childish innocence and confidence, in spite of the stumps of his teeth. His clothing was old and stiff with dirt and he stood at the door of his indescribable house like a wizened subterranean man at the entrance to a catacomb. I followed him into an odorous confusion that was slippy underfoot.

It was very dark inside and there was a sound of heavy breathing. A bulky shape moved. 'My cow,' said Hamish. This was the first of two rooms. In it lived the cow and some hens. We moved through an aperture into Hamish's apartment.

Pieces of wood projected from the walls and the thatch

and it was extremely difficult not to knock against them. Two windows let in a glimmer of light but it took some time to become accustomed to the gloom after the brilliance outside. A fire burned on the floor and the peat smoke, which had no proper chimney, made its way vaguely to a hole in the roof and swirled in the semi-darkness. The windows were green with mould. Cobwebs, engrained with dirt, hung in festoons. On the walls grew weeds and fungi.

I sat on a wooden bench under one of the windows. The peat reek was so thick that the opposite wall was invisible. The chair that Hamish occupied was solidly embedded in the ground. Dirt, refuse, old food and ashes had slowly risen till the chair was gripped half-way up its legs.

He gave me the story of his life. It came out as a set-piece. Since he had been a boy he had lived alone. An odd job as a carrier with the village shop had helped him to buy bread and tea. Most of his meals were bread and tea. His hens allowed him an egg now and then, but as they contrived to lay anywhere within a hundred yards of the house few eggs were ever found. He offered to boil me an egg, and seemed to expect my refusal.

He was apologetic about his health. He had been hale and strong for forty years and could not understand how his health had suddenly failed. He said he was just fifty but his eyes, almost blind with cataract, and his twisted limbs made him look eighty. He said he thought his health had broken because of the burden of the magic he possessed.

He had been offered a bed in an institution but would not take it. He thought he would not be allowed home again. In any case it was impossible to go. 'My cow she is going to calve next month and it would not do for me to leave her.

And when I was away they might perhaps pull my house down. They tell me it is not clean but I do not want to leave.'

A duck waddled across the floor and he fed it with bits of bread, speaking softly in Gaelic. Then he blinked through the smoke and said that his duck spoke to him.

'Some people do not believe me when I tell them and say it is an old man's foolishness, but my duck is wise. She does not understand English: no, just the Gaelic. She is a very wise duck but I am afraid she is not well. She has not been laying for many days.'

He had second-sight. When he was a boy he had been watching a funeral. He happened to tread heavily on the foot of a woman next to him. He apologized, hoping he had not hurt her. 'No,' she said, 'you have done more hurt to yourself.' This accidental contact had passed the second-sight to him. 'It is not good for a man to know the future, it is the cause of much unhappiness. That is how I did hurt to myself. Sometimes I see things, like a vision, someone dying perhaps, or bad fortune.'

'Can you see the future whenever you wish?' I asked.

'No, not with second-sight. It comes perhaps when I am working or eating. Just for a moment like a picture. It has not come for a long time and I am glad. Telling about the future is not second-sight. Oh, no, that is fortune-telling. The tea leaves can be read sometimes.'

Hamish decided he could not tell my fortune. He swilled some tea in a cup but the leaves did not satisfy him. He said the hour was wrong.

He had another way of telling a person's fortune, more interesting and to me quite new. Unfortunately, the laws relating to the printed word prevent me putting it down on paper.

I dropped in at a smithy in Appin to escape the rain. There was a maelstrom of steam and smoke inside the building. A huge man in a leather apron was striking an anvil with a mighty hammer. 'Come in,' he said in the neat English of the west.

There were two smiths. They apologized for the atmosphere; there was something wrong with the flue. They spoke as hosts apologizing to a guest for some inconvenience. They had a rural tidiness of thought and gesture and their manners were gracious.

At the door was a dump of old horse-shoes. It had accumulated over two years. In the old days six months would have produced a larger pile. The older smith blamed motors and tractors. The younger smith blamed nothing but said that he was going to Glasgow in winter to look for a job. They worked as they spoke and when they had finished a set of shoes they hung them on a rack and brewed a pot of tea. The older man, built in the tradition of mighty smiths, dealt with the domestic detail. With his hammer on one side he was as delicate as an old maid in her parlour. The tea was black and very hot. They drained their cups almost at a gulp and then took another bar of iron from the fire. I asked them many questions and they replied courteously. They did not ask a single question about myself. That too was courtesy. The rain stopped and I went on.

I went into the bar of an inn one evening. There had been a celebration in the village—a marriage—and the men were out to prolong the festivities. When I joined them they had reached the stage of argument. Tongues were eloquent on whether the Macdonalds of Skye had fought at Culloden. One group held that the Macdonalds were cowards and did not appear. The others claimed that the Macdonalds left the field before battle because of some mistake in clan precedence. One man said the Macdonalds had fought well and with gallantry.

'Gentlemen, gentlemen. It is a small wonder that Culloden was lost—black be the day—if the followers of the Prince fight amongst themselves. What would you do if Tearlach walked in here now?'

This was too much for a fuddled materialist. 'That is impossible. You are foolish, Willie. Tearlach—Prince Charles Edward Stuart—has been dead far too long.'

'Dead or not dead I don't give a damn'—this was a strong anti-Macdonald—'You're drunk, Willie. You'll be telling us that the railways are giving cheap tickets to Culloden for the Highland army.'

Willie winked solemnly. 'What do you think, doctor?' he said to a man sitting under the window.

The doctor raised his glass. 'I think, gentlemen, we are bordering on the metaphysical.'

There was a roar of laughter. 'Ach, the doctor always has the last word.'

Arthur was another who was thinking of changing his job. He was a cattleman on a farm in central Perthshire. In the house the farmer's wife talked of going 'east' and 'west' when she went from one room to another. It was an old custom. 'Come away east' she said to bring a person from the sitting-room to the kitchen.

Arthur wanted a change for the sake of experience.

'There's naethin tae beat a change o' scenery afore ye're ruited in the grund. It's a graunt education and I'm not complainin' o' bein' here. He's a guid man I'm fee'd to an' I winna go till there's someone suited to tak' my place.'

There was a dance in the barn one evening. The barn was a lofty building above the byre. From its raftered roof Arthur had hung Christmas decorations. He had tied sprigs of fern and bracken to the walls. This was a precaution against midges 'an other beasties. What wi' bein' above the coos ye canna be too careful.'

Shortly before eight (long enough after the last milking to let people change their clothes) the party began to arrive. The men were newly shaven, stiffly erect in their Sunday suit of blue worsted. The women eyed each other's dresses, talking and giggling. A few elderly people came in, old wives who sat on trestles against the wall. They smiled schemingly on the younger people. Their husbands were in a different mood, dour of feature, half reluctant to be seen at a barn frolic.

The band struck up a Paul Jones. There was a fiddle, a piano-accordion, a mouth-organ, a trumpet and a Jew's harp. The Paul Jones ended.

'Jock, man, you havena forgot the pipes?'

The pipes were lifted from a black box. At the first chord there was a yell and a thudding of feet. The floor trembled. It had been swept that afternoon but the dust of years was dislodged and rose in a fine swirl. The solid building shook. The lamps hanging from the rafters began to tremble.

Jock's fingers jumped up and down on the chanter. His right foot stabbed the floor in rhythm. His playing became gradually faster and faster. The dancers set and linked and 'hooched'. Court shoes and great boots danced to each other. The pipes wailed into silence.

Bottles of beer were uncorked and lemonade was poured into glasses. The men wiped their brows and tilted the bottles. The girls, with dishevelled hair, swallowed the lemonade and said what a fine dance it was.

Beyond the good farmland of the straths, across the central Highland massif, there is the crofting country on the rim of the mainland and on the islands. The crofter has caught the imagination of people outside the Highlands. A good life, fresh air and honest work, they think. There is independence and freedom, they think, their minds moved by the dim memory of a Victorian oleograph showing a picturesque thatched croft under a sunlit hill.

It is true, after a fashion. There is independence and freedom as long as the economics of crofting can pay the way. There is a greater sense of mature self-reliance than one finds in the cities or the organized rural areas. If a man has only a score of neighbours within twenty miles he must have the stuff of independence in him, or he would have departed long ago. But for many it is a diminishing freedom, since the age is against the individual setting up as a working unit sufficient unto himself.

Crofting has often been a means to an end, working itself out in the second and third generation, so that an old man in his chimney corner counts his blessings—the eldest son a judge on circuit in the colonies, the second a 'head of department' in Whitehall, the third a professor of medicine in a university. That was a pattern of fulfilment that very many crofts produced, and do so to-day. As long as crofting can pay, only one outside service is essential—education.

The lives of people are eloquent. The city man, commuting by tram from his brick suburban cell to his concrete office, the miner walking from his cottage to the pit-head, the mechanic taking the bus from his lodging to his work-bench—they are the dispossessed of the twentieth century. Like animals pacing up and down a cage they move freely for the length of the 'run' and no more; the bus ride, the tram journey, the vertical drop into the earth, measure the length of their leash. Sleep and food is at one end, work is at the other, and that is life's pattern.

Instead of a sense of community there is the crowd at the football match or the party meeting; instead of a deep-rooted culture there is the cinema; instead of the outdoor challenge of the seasons there is the lie-abed challenge of the football pool or the cash-in-advance hilarity of the holiday camp. These sorts of contrasts are the stock-in-trade of every sociologist who seeks to enlighten his fellows.

In comparison the crofter has escaped the degradation of the cities. He has something of a pioneer's freedom and pays for it in the way stubborn stony ground rots away a man's ambition. But he is a wiser, more rounded character. The crofter and his fellow Highlanders are engaged in a losing battle against the civilization of the cities. The croft is not simply an alternative to the routine of pay-check and union-card. It is often the preliminary. And there are many in the Highlands who do not croft.

Hamish, in his 'black house', can only keep going by a retreat into early senility. The younger smith in Appin is about to be sucked into the industrial maw of Glasgow and will get a job building battleships for Britain. The carousing men in the village pub are probably all on the county pay-roll already, and they fight a maudlin rear-action with their staunch ally History. Arthur, the cattleman, has never been able to set up on his own. It is his ambition but he thinks it will be impossible to find the place and the cash. And he is restless in any case. His independence is now what his boss allows him, so he chooses his bosses carefully. The girls at the dance nearly all want to marry and go to the cities.

Occasionally an individual wins through to preserve the independence that he values. One man who lives in a region in the west found that he could no longer make a living from the croft that he had taken over from his father. He was faced with two choices. He could either go south to the cities of Scotland or England. Or he could hire himself out to a local 'boss', such as a hydro-electric board, or a road-making contractor. But he had no intention of leaving his own country and wild horses would not make him work as the paid servant of another man. There was only one way in which he could support himself, stay in his house, and live the life he liked. He became a poacher.

He has done rather well. He has a lorry and goes out at night to shoot deer. He drives the dead beasts to a town where he has a 'contact'. In his own community, scattered along the coast of a sea-loch, he is still a crofter. The local policeman is one of his best friends. They chat to each other in Gaelic and because it would be bad manners the policeman never asks how the poaching is coming on.

Chapter Fifteen

TO RELISH THE ECCENTRIC

H UGH MACDIARMID PROBABLY HIT the nail on the head when he wrote in his book *Scottish Eccentrics*:

The eccentric actually becomes the typical, and the wildest irregularities combine to manifest the essence of our national spirit and historical function.

The use of phrases like 'national spirit and historic function' is itself one of the more engaging eccentricities of the Scots.

It is tempting to read deeply into Scottish eccentricity, because the fiercer and more voluble Scots insist on eccentricity as a significant national trait and have even gone to the trouble of creating a special term to describe it—*Caledonian Antisyzygy*. This gives a pleasantly mysterious label to the mixture of hard-headedness and romanticism, to the perverse pursuit of lost causes and the stubborn pursuit of efficiency, which some people claim to be particularly Scottish.

The picture of the Scot as a kilted Janus is a popular one; it is full of self-flattery. It suggests—as one must assume the fiercer nationalists intend to suggest—that the Scot is a man apart, not necessarily more virtuous or more vicious, but endowed with his virtues and vices in permutations which are not normal throughout the rest of the world. Put in a blunt fundamental proposition this attitude emerges as a vulgar exclamation, 'Here's tae us, whae's like us? De'il the yin'.

Why there should be many Scots who harp with dogged asperity on their differences from other people is another question. Why they should elevate these differences, once they have isolated them, into majestic portents of national merit, is a matter that might engage the psychologist and the anthropologist. Eccentricity as a national characteristic is the field of the voluble minority of Scots who profess to interpret their country to their fellows. Eccentricity as an engaging, or sometimes displeasing, personal attribute is frequently encountered, but probably not more frequently than elsewhere.

It is a matter of behaviour, or pursuing principles to egocentric conclusions. The spirit of compromise, which is the tactful basis of English genius, is not understood by the Scot who likes to think he would not forgo his principles to obtain an advantage. (A small exception to this happened when the price of whisky had soared and stocks had diminished. A publican was asked why he was charging a higher price for what seemed to be a smaller glass. 'Well, you see,' he said, holding up the glass and looking at the half-inch of Highland dew, 'you might call this a measure of expediency.')

Without pursuing eccentricity into the realms of a national *ethos*, one might well look for a moment at a few of the more engaging eccentrics. Robert Louis Stevenson was torn between righteous puritanism and the warm pleasures that he enjoyed in the less reputable houses of Leith Walk in Edinburgh. Not an eccentric himself he made an exaggerated literary eccentric in the dual character of Dr Jekyll and Mr Hyde.

The Scots have often confused their villains and their heroes. When Stevenson made one man both hero and villain he created a very Scottish personality, especially the sense of guilt about the sense of pleasure. There was an historic parallel. 'Bonnie Dundee' and 'Bloody Claverhouse' were the same person: the name depended on the point of view.

One of the most roystering and joyful characters who have appeared on the Scottish scene was a Father John Damian. He was not strictly Scottish but he was an adventurer of the early Renaissance, a period when nationality was more or less a matter of domicile. He was a flamboyant and practical eccentric in an age when the norm of behaviour was more elastic than it is now. He was the type of brilliant impostor whose great gestures and grandiloquence would no longer be believed (or would lead to a cold hearing in a court of law) because we have lost the innocence of credulity, just as we have lost the capacity for the heroic attitude. Father John Damian could not inhabit an age where an impostor cannot believe even in himself.

The brilliant cleric was a favourite of the brilliant court

of James IV. He was a rogue and a scholar, a combination that is always as interesting as it is frequent. When he came to Scotland his enemies called him a 'Turk of Tartar', and in doing this they were a little inaccurate. Though he had started as one, by the time he arrived in Edinburgh Father John was no longer a Turk in the sense of being a Mohammedan. He had forsworn the Prophet and embraced Christianity in France, a change of faith that was accomplished by slaying a monk and wearing his clothes. He professed skill as a doctor, a 'French leich'. It is probable the man was not altogether a scoundrel because King James had a Stuart facility for intellectual baggage—'skilled in medicine and the sciences, and well versed in theological studies'—and might have detected an impostor. But the Stuarts were notoriously bad judges of men, and in any case King James was young and gay and it may have amused him to encourage a charlatan.

The Scottish Lord High Treasurer provided Father Damian, after his arrival, with a 'gown of damask lined with budge', a tapestried bed, blankets and sheets of linen, scarlet hose and velvet trousers. Damian's name was written in the expenses list concerning the building of a furnace and the provision of plant for alchemical research, an engagement which he undertook with the Master of Works.

The research covered the two hoary and time-honoured mysteries, firstly, the transmuting of base metal into gold, and secondly, the provision of the elixir of life. The Master of Works and Father Damian proposed to combine the two objectives and produce one comprehensive and vital solution. Amongst the ingredients were quicksilver, wine, brandy, vinegar, alum, salt and eggs. The pair were successful to the extent of manufacturing a kind of egg-nog that was nourishing as well as intoxicating.

In 1508 the irrepressible Father undertook to launch himself in flight. By then he had played the role of Master of the Royal Revels and held the post of paymaster at Stirling Castle, besides being the companion of the King at shooting matches which he usually won, the prize being paid by the national exchequer.

Damian jumped from the wall of Stirling Castle with his home-made wings strapped around him. He was very lucky. Instead of killing himself he broke a thigh-bone, and afterwards he explained his failure by the fact that he had stupidly included in the wings some feathers of domestic hens 'which yearn and covet the midden and not the skies'.

In comparison with Damian, the life of Thomas Edward, the nineteenth-century naturalist, is a record of sober and industrious eccentricity. There is nothing flamboyant, nothing wasteful, no playing to the gallery. Edward had the eccentricity of the stubborn; he pursued a private passion to the limit of human perseverance.

Edward's character, replete with the virtues beloved by Victorian moralists, persuaded Samuel Smiles, the Victorian delineator of virtue, to write the history of the man, *The Story of a Scotch Naturalist*. This book is not only a study of Edward but is a relentless exposure of Smiles's devotion to his ideas of moral behaviour. One is hardly certain if Smiles approved of what Edward did: he doted on the way it was done.

Thomas Edward lived nearly all his life in poverty, an obscure cobbler in the north-east of Scotland. He was born into a poor family and from infancy he had a love of 'beasts'—anything from a worm to a pig. At the age of two he was found asleep under a breeding sow. His early upbringing by hostile, ignorant, but severely affectionate parents, with no understanding of his unusual tastes, set a pattern that he was to know for the greater part of his long life. Though his parents loved him in a dour uncompromising fashion they beat him in a way that to-day would lead to court. He could not be cured of his wicked delight in crabs and leeches and toads and sticklebacks. He stayed away all night many times, became dangerously ill with a fever, and as soon as he re-covered—after being gently nursed by his mother—his first conscious question was about the welfare of his mouse and his crabs and the other creatures that he had hidden in bottles and boxes. He was ill for three months. When he was cured, he roamed the countryside again—streams, mill-dams, woods, hedges—and was again thrashed by his father. According to Smiles this took place about the age of four.

Before he was five he went to the first of his schools and began to play truant. He loved the fish-market because of the flies and the beetles and the rats. He took insects and animals into school. Time and time again he was beaten and punished, but his determination was hardened.

He was transferred to another school where a master was an expert with the tawse—a long leather strap cut into tails and hardened in the fire, a weapon which (along with the Shorter Catechism) has brought up many generations of Scots. He was subjected to a system of brutal treatment that would have broken any but the most stubborn boy. On the hands, on the back, over his body, he was lashed by a furious young schoolmaster.

At the age of six, after being expelled from three schools,

he refused to go to a fourth and was sent to work instead. His passion for living things developed. It included growing things. Eventually it included all objects in the natural world, alive or not.

When he was a young man he learned something of cobbling from a drunken tyrant of a master (in Smiles's book vice is underlined to enhance virtue). He joined the militia. During a drill parade he broke rank to chase a butterfly. He was pursued and caught. The conversation is Smiles's:

'Looking Edward sternly in the face, the corporal said, "What's up, Edward?" "Nothing." "The deuce!" "No, it wasn't that, it was a splendid butterfly." "A butter-devil!" "No! it was a butter-*fly*!" "Stuff!" said the corporal; "are you mad?" "No; I don't think I am."'

Edward married, was employed as a journeyman cobbler, and began to produce a family. Every moment away from his cobbler's stool he spent in the countryside. He slept as and when he could and when it was necessary. Without any scientific education, or any access to it, he built up a mass of knowledge from his own observation of birds, flowers, stones, trees, insects, animals. Later in life he wrote his testament:

Everything that moves or lives, everything that grows, everything created or formed by the hand or the will of the Omnipotent, has such a fascinating charm for me, and sends such a thrill of pleasure through my whole frame, that to describe my feelings is utterly impossible.

By the time he was thirty-one or so he had preserved 2,000 specimens of living creatures. According to Smiles there were 'quadrupeds, birds, reptiles, fishes, crustacea, star-fish, zoophytes, corals, sponges' and a huge number of plants. Some were in bottles, but most were in cases.

In order to make the smaller cases he bought boxes from the merchants; and in breaking them up he usually got as many nails as would serve to nail the new cases together. To make the larger cases he bought wood from the carpenters. He papered the insides, painted the outsides, and glazed the whole of the cases himself. . . . There were about 300 cases in all.

He exhibited his collection in Banff in 1845 and 'took the inhabitants by surprise', even though his 2,000 plants could not be shown (a collection made over eight years) because the preserved specimens, in their huge box, had been used as a lair by cats and the lot had to be burned.

He decided to hold an exhibition in Aberdeen, 'the centre of northern intellect and business'; and from the proceeds he hoped to open a shop for the 'employment and provision' of his family and buy himself a microscope and other instruments. The exhibition was a failure. Edward was too proud to ask for help and too unbending to accept what was offered him.

Smiles finds the exhibition an admirable opportunity for painting the picture of the virtuous workman. There are pages of uplifting conversation. Edward, manipulated by Smiles, becomes a bit of a prig. Someone says to him that he 'has never heard of such a thing' as a workman making a collection of natural objects, to which Edward agrees that the labouring people 'do not go into the fields to drink in the sweets of nature, but rush unthinkingly into the portals of hell, and drown their sorrows in whisky. In this way they beggar themselves and pauperize their families.'

Edward almost pauperized his family through the failure of the exhibition which had been taken to Aberdeen in six carriers' carts. He sold his collection to pay expenses and went back to Banff, as Smiles put it, 'ruined, disappointed, beggared—his aims and hopes of life blasted'.

He took to his old habits. The years passed. He began to write articles, made a few useful friends, and began to be known. Apart from his friends, who were mostly ministers, he was surrounded by an abysmal ignorance that did not understand him. He was still working as a shoemaker. He lived a great deal on water and oatmeal. When his wife boiled an egg it was a luxury. At the age of forty-four, when he had built up another collection, he fell ill and had to sell 'upwards of forty cases of birds . . . together with three hundred specimens of mosses and marine plants' to keep himself and his family and pay the doctor's bills.

He recovered but had to acquire gentler habits. There could be no more tumbling down cliffs in pursuit of a rare bird. His main interest became marine zoology. The rural cobbler wrote for the Linnean Society Journal and in the end he was elected an associate. He was eventually credited with discovering twenty-six new species amongst zoophytes, molluscs and fishes. He ended his days as an aged shoemaker, his virtues blazoned to the world by Smiles, and impressive tributes, mostly on paper, pouring on him from all corners of the world.

With Thomas Edward the eccentricity was the man. Without it he would have been nothing. He had an unusual capacity for the exceptional. There is a simpler eccentricity in not letting the right hand know what the left hand is doing. This kind of moral duplicity, unrecorded by Smiles, has been practised by the Scots as successfully as by anyone else. John Knox, the paragon of the Reformation, wrote

The First Blast of the Trumpet Against the Monstrous Regiment of Women. The Argument was not quite so compelling as the title, nor was there any second blast. It is hardly necessary to complete the picture of Knox as a man of furtive pleasures, dallying with wenches in dark corners.

The gallery of eccentrics is extensive. There was a country laird, John Clerk, who had never been to sea. He wrote an essay on naval tactics which appears to have been accepted by the British Navy and which influenced the course of sea-battles during the eighteenth century. Lord Monboddo, a Scottish law lord of some ability, believed, or pretended to believe, that everyone was born with a tail and this was not generally known because of the conspiracy amongst doctors and midwives who cut off the tails at birth. Monboddo used to arrive at confinements to look at babies immediately after they were born. 'Ach, ye've foiled me again' he cried to the midwife when he saw the tail-less posteriors.

Eccentricity survives, less artlessly perhaps than in the past, because a man must consciously develop his personality against the mass influences of the age. It is not so much the bee in the bonnet—an insect to which everyone is entitled—that makes the eccentric; it is the insistence on personal values, not so much a trespass against conventional behaviour as an indifference to it.

There is a story of a recent eccentric. He was a retired doctor who kept a small pig in an ordinary room of his house so that he might answer those who asked him why he did so: 'To remind me that there are more wholesome creatures than men.' It may have come to this, that the eccentric no longer embellishes society, but makes his gestures as a protest against it.

Chapter Sixteen

TO LO'E THE LASSES

Down by the burn, where scented birks
Wi' dew are hanging clear, my jo,
I'll meet thee on the lea rig,
My ain kind dearie, O.
—Burns.

THERE WAS ONCE A conversation conducted in the deep leather chairs of an Edinburgh club. A visiting *littérateur*, anxious to perform a pretty phrase after lunch, said with slow pomp over his coffee: 'That you should revere as a national poet a man who could entitle a poem "The lass that made the bed to me" suggests that your Scottish muse is a professional trollop.'

The answer was short and chuckling and cast in the Doric:

'Ay, maybe, but sic a kind, bonny trollop!' And the ghost of Rabelais smiled over the coffee-cups.

Panurge and Pantagruel are not noticeably Scottish. Gargantua, the civilized monarch, never wore a Highland man's breeks. But Rabelais, as translated into English by Sir Thomas Urquhart, remains the most astonishing product of the Franco-Scottish alliance. Sir Thomas was a Scotsman of Cromarty, but he was also a King's man and went south to fight with the Royalists. He regretted the way in which the status of his country had fallen after the union of the crowns and did not appreciate that his own 'retreat to the south' in support of his monarch was part of the dissipation of the strength of Scotland. Scores like him, the natural leaders of politics and culture, took the high road to England and then bemoaned the impoverishment of their own country. At the battle of Worcester Sir Thomas was unfortunate enough to lose some of his manuscripts, but not his Rabelais. The first two books of his masterpiece appeared the year after he published his *Vindication of the Honour of Scotland*.

There is almost as much of Sir Thomas as of Rabelais in the translation. He expanded, embellished, inflated the sometimes thinner French prose with an invention and idiom that raised him to joint-creator. The flavour was recognizably Scottish. It exists, for example, in David Lindsay's Satyre of the Three Estaites, which, edited by Robert Kemp for 'length and breadth', was recently played for the first time in five hundred years to a delighted and enthusiastic audience in Edinburgh. The flavour occurs in Burns, and again in Lewis Grassic Gibbon's *Scots Quair* of the nineteen-thirties. It is doubtful if there could be good Scots writing without it.

Where English writing becomes excruciatingly arch and naughty or wittily indecorous, Scots has remained faithful, in its fitful fashion, to a Chaucerian saltiness. This unambiguous honesty has been frequently banished altogether, according to the varying moral tastes of the centuries. But its lustiness endures, like the nature of man himself.

The Scotswoman, in fiction and out of it, has had varied fortunes. At the end of the international brilliance of the Scottish court in the sixteenth century the Scottish dame of high degree and amenability disappeared. Even Sir Thomas did not dare recast his story in Scotland. The dame's sisters went to pasture and were discovered in lush fields, some time later, by Alan Ramsay. The ladies had become lassies.

> Haith, ye're ill-bred, he'll smilin' say
> Ye'll worry me, ye greedy rook;
> Syne frae your arms she'll rin away,
>   And hide hersel in some dark neuk.
> Her lauch will lead ye to the place,
>   Where lies the happiness ye want;
> And plainly tell ye to your face
>   Nineteen say-nays are hauf a grant.

The shepherd lassie was often presented as primly and properly as a piece of Dresden, though less coldly fragile. She was dandified out of her native language and no longer 'cam ower the knowes'.

> I might have been a prince's peer,
>   When I came over the knowes,
> Till the shepherd boy beguiled me,
>   Milking my daddy's ewes.

She was so unreal that she could not survive and is now, in that guise, a pretty period piece. Those fair tenders of fleecy frocks may not have reflected Scottish womanhood but they suited new tastes for elegance rather than for honesty. The bucolic or the coy, whose lustiness was a careful literary device, offered little real warmth. There was a chill over Scotland, not yet to be dispelled; and people like James Boswell found it more profitable to pursue their sophisticated pleasures in London where there was substance as well as elegant shadow.

Then came Robert Burns who took the pastoral lassie, tumbled her in the hay, and turned her once again into a recognizable wench. The Scots girl of poetry was on her own feet again, which meant that she was very often on her back. She was passionate, bonny, sometimes crude, but wonderfully human.

Earthier than his well-known love poems were Burns's priapic poems, published under the title of *The Merry Muses of Caledonia*. They were taken from the folk tradition of bawdy balladry and recast by the poet.

But times changed again. Sir Walter Scott, who in many ways was a passionless prelude to Victorianism, quite lost sight of the girl with the kilted skirts. By the middle of last century she was banished again, with not even a porcelain replica to take her place. Not till Lewis Grassic Gibbon wrote his *Cloud Howe* did she emerge once more in her full magnificent stature in literature. It was immediately obvious that she had been hiding with the poor and the honest who always made her welcome. In Gibbon's fields and farmyards she stretches her arms and lets the sun and the wind and the lads of Kinraddie enjoy her immortality.

Beating their hard hands against the tradition of amorous

laisser faire has been a succession of puritans, females many of them, the Mrs MacGrundy's of Willa Muir's book, *Mrs Grundy in Scotland*. Under their iron rule the unspeakable and the unmentionable did not merit even a dash of asterisks. Sin lurked everywhere, behind the haystack and in the kitchen closet.

For a long time Scottish writing, reflecting the social scene, behaved as though its authors lacked the essential senses. Biographers of Burns, anxious to sanctify their earthy human hero, went to a great deal of trouble to 'prove' that he could not have been the author of *The Merry Muses*. The anti-traditionalists, the Mrs MacGrundys, busied themselves far beyond their ordinary spheres of influence. An inability to countenance pleasure in any innocent form became the standard of conduct for small groups of fanatical kill-joys. The narrower forms of religion throve avidly in this misery of the spirit. As recently as the nineteen-thirties a Scottish minister of the Wee Free Kirk was banished from his pulpit because he accepted hospitality in a house where children were having a Christmas party and he *made no effort* to end the unseemly and wanton behaviour of drinking lemonade and playing with toy balloons. In vain did he plead that he took no part in the party. Because he did not oppose it vigorously, as one deals with the devil, he lost his job as a preacher.

With Urquhart and his genial successors on the one hand, and the unfrocked minister on the other, it is not surprising that the country which bred both should have evolved a varied approach to the relations of man and woman.

It has never been difficult to tie the connubial knot in

Scotland, and until recently it was possible to tie a slip-knot which either partner could undo at will. One of the types of 'irregular' marriage was hand-fasting, or trial marriage. It was a popular union in the Borders. After co-habiting for a year and a day the couple separated if the marriage had not proved mutually satisfactory. Hand-fasting was a most progressive attempt to recognize that maladjustments of temperament should be discovered before the union was made secure. This style of marriage, with an escape clause, was recognized by the law, though not by the Church. Hand-fasting had an ancient and honourable lineage and was descended from the Anglo-Saxon practices, in which marriage was a secular institution, an arrangement between families to be made and broken with the consent of the parties. Until it disappeared from Scotland the law made provision for it, and was able to deal with any children that had been born.

Hand-fasting was related to the easy entry into the lady's 'bower' which the lordly swain enjoyed in Scottish songs and ballads. Not very far beneath the literary surface there was the reality of enforced marriage, of the *Jus Primae Noctis*, of barons who kept their serfs replenished on a 'stud' principle, of the notorious inquisitional Church in the puritan centuries when the least deviation from the narrow path of righteousness met with public censure, torture and sometimes death. It was after the age of godly torment that some of the most famous love songs became known. Some were refined and genteel, and when the puritan severity lessened they were heard in the salons of decorous merchants and their families. Others reeked of the barnyard, or were delicately perfumed with hawthorn.

Gin ye meet a bonnie lassie,
Gie her a kiss and let her gae;
But gin ye meet a dirty hizzie,
Fye, gar rub her o'er wi strae.

Hand-fasting has vanished, and so have many other types of so-called 'irregular' marriage that lasted until they were abolished by a 1940 Act of Parliament. 'Regular' marriage is marriage by a parson. All that is left of 'irregular' marriage is a ceremony in a registrar's office.

What has happened is that a bright feature of Scottish life has disappeared. This was the right of a man and a woman to join *themselves* in matrimony. Nowadays they must be married by someone, a minister or a registrar.

Declaration before a witness built the fame of Gretna Green. The romantic fables that have become attached to Gretna suggest that the marriage performed there was of an emergency nature. It was not so. The marriage was normal and legal and might have been performed anywhere in Scotland before any witness. There was no advantage possessed by Gretna that did not exist in Aberdeen or Kirkintilloch. Gretna built its reputation because it was strategically situated to deal with English runaway couples anxious to evade the pursuit of irate parents who had withheld consent. The smith at Gretna must have appeared a miraculous dispenser of the matrimonial state.

The practice became so popular with young couples that potentially irate English parents became alarmed. In 1856 the path of true love was made a little less smooth. It became necessary for one of the contracting parties to reside in Scotland for at least three weeks before the marriage. But the useful facility of mutual declaration remained for cash customers, and even though a similar marriage could be performed anywhere in Scotland those who arrived breathlessly at the Gretna anvil believed they were undertaking a unique union.

All that has changed. Romance has now to go through the usual channels. The Gretna marriage was, from another point of view, a complicated ceremony. It involved a third party. Scottish custom also recognized, perhaps for the specially bashful and the specially brazen, that marriage was a private undertaking and, once a couple had made up their minds, a third party witness was unlikely to add force to their intentions. 'Habit and repute' was a form of marriage legally valid, though sometimes difficult to establish at law. Its basis was co-habitation and the willingness of the spouses to be regarded as husband and wife. Simplicity could hardly be further simplified. In certain strata of society it was not always expedient to advertise that a union was fortified only by 'habit and repute' and a couple sometimes found it socially expedient to reinforce their bliss with a more authoritative and public ceremony. But 'habit and repute' had understandable attractions as a union, whatever the neighbours might think. At times, however, the views of the neighbours have been sought if one of the reputed swains tried to deny the marriage. If the local grocer believed that he had been serving his wares to Mrs So-and-so, and not to Miss So-and-so, then the fact of marriage was established.

Behind the customs is the rural meaning of a woman's worth in her ability to provide children. Hand-fasting was formal recognition of this. In various guises trial marriage was practised in Scotland, as in most other countries, and numberless swains blessed the liberal attitude that encouraged their ardent wooing. Marriage was the objective, for the purpose of raising a family as it said in the Good Book. The sequence of wedding and bedding was reasonably inverted.

Orkney has received some notoriety because of 'bundling', a curious custom about which there is still some mystery. Inclement northern weather out of doors and lack of accommodation indoors is said to have made it difficult for a couple to find privacy and comfort for wooing. Bundling was a social device in which the girl was tied tightly, often by her mother, in a single outer garment believed to be impenetrable. She was then deposited in the sleeping-recess or box-bed of her parent's home and her Lothario climbed in beside her. The insistence of the apologists on the chaste morality of bundling is certainly not in accord with the robust tradition of the country.

A Victorian writer, somewhat diffidently mentioning the subject in a book on Scotland's northern islands, found it necessary to say that 'at the present day the morality of the islands is alleged to be up to the standard of the most moral parts of Scotland, although a custom, similar to what is known as "bundling" in Wales, has long been prevalent'. He cannot have inquired too closely or he would have found the same name in use in the north. In a book called *Popular Antiquities* the custom is described as one 'in which the betrothing parties go to bed in their clothes. It has given rise to many actions for seduction.'

Chapter Seventeen

TO SAVOUR SENTIMENT

'A sporran is a lapsed beard.'—Timothy Shy.

THERE WAS A SCOT who said, 'I love my country. I love every inch of it passionately. If there were no people in it I'd love it even more.'

One knows what he had in mind. A picture of the Scots-man has gone forth to the world—a man cutting a comic caper, wearing a brief kilt and a red nose, brandishing a crooked stick and a bottle of whisky. No people have guyed themselves more mercilessly than the Scots, and then been appalled that a foreigner does not believe they exist at all outside a music-hall.

At home, in Scotland, there is the type of Scot who takes his Scottishness in constant small doses, like salts, to keep his patriotic blood in condition. He belongs to a Burns' club and annually swears fealty to a poet he has never thoroughly read and quite misunderstands. He mildly worships haggis, Bonnie Prince Charlie, and bagpipes. His wife wraps her sturdy Scottish haunches in a tartan skirt, unaware that a female in anything resembling a kilt is anathema.

In a profitable way the Scot has prostituted his Scottishness. Extirpated from his Highland glens and Lowland valleys, confined within a brick box in a city suburb, his values have changed. He has come to worship the meretricious in his nation. In a theatre he applauds the most grotesque modern travesty of a Scotsman—the Scots commedian. Where Scottishness remains true to type, in the rural areas, a Scots comedian would find a stony unappreciative audience. In the Highlands where he dare not trespass with his ill-fitting kilt and his cosmetic inebriation, he would be ignored, which is the politest insult of all.

The Scots comedian is the symbol of the way in which robust natural traditions become perverted and sentimentalized when they are cultivated in cities. The symbol of national pride and vigour—the peer of John Bull, Uncle Sam and Marianne—is a Scottish professional figure of fun, an unsteady scarecrow on a stage. (The true comedians of Scotland, men like Duncan Macrae or the late Tommy Lorne, are of a different tradition of vigorous and glorious theatre, in a class far apart from the second-rate funsters with whisky bottles and tottering steps.)

The acceptance of the second-rate is symptomatic of something pernicious. Behind the dourness of the Scots is a reservoir of emotion. When this is broached it can pour out in a torrent of sentimentality. The Scot, homely, reserved, with few words, is a familiar, even a reliable, person. The Scot in his cups is tolerable, and may sometimes approach greatness and eloquence. The Scot in tears is an appalling piece of human wreckage.

The worst excesses of Scottish sentimentality occur in Glasgow. The blame has been laid on the vast Irish immigration (is not Glasgow known as the capital of Ireland?) but that does not change the diagnosis of the Celtic disease. Some of the newspapers printed in the west of Scotland carry In Memoriam columns in which appear tear-jerkers even cruder than an onion, as though the deep emotions which man reserves for the solemn occasions of life had become as meretricious as the celluloid emotions of a film.

> *A little tribute, true and tender,*
> *Just to show we still remember.*

Or:

> *Not gone from daddy's memory*
> *Not gone from mummy's love,*
> *But gone to be an angel*
> *In the heavenly home above.*

For people whose countrymen have produced songs of exquisite pathos, these lachrymose lines record the downfall of a race. How differently it was done in the past. There is an epitaph in a rural graveyard on the shores of the Firth of Forth:

> *In this churchyard lies Eppie Coutts,*
> *Either here or hereabouts;*
> *But whaur she is there's nane can tell,*
> *Till Eppie rise and tell hersell.*

As distinct from a dry expression of feeling in the country-side, it would be reasonable to expect a sophisticated soufflé in the cities. But in matters less grievous than grief this is not so. Emotion remains a serious thing. One must either go very sparingly with it, or deal with it as a child deals with strawberry jam. When the Scot loses the sparse natural discipline of his country environment, he becomes a child. He goes to extraordinary lengths in stretching his national feelings, like an old-fashioned confectioner stretching a skein of toffee. The intention is worthy. The country is a nation in name only. Its parliament has gone. It is ruled from London. All that remains of essential Scottishness must, therefore, be thrice guarded.

A new deal for Scotland, a parliament in Edinburgh and a modified national autonomy, all that is wrapped up with the politics of Scotland, would be a kind and essential step in saving the Scot from himself. Until this is achieved the Scottishness has to be summoned by artificial gatherings, *ad hoc* celebrations, decorated with tartan and infused with pipe music. When the Scot announces his Scottishness to the world, imploring the tourist to visit his land, he does so with a poster showing a beefy piper and in the background a sunny scene of Highland games. His national spirit has become a spectacle, and to enjoy it a ticket of admission must be purchased.

Highland Games are an intriguing way of pretending that the Highland way of life is a blend of physical prowess and colourful pageantry, a peep-show of tartan with strong men wrestling with lumps of timber like telegraph poles under the drone and fury of massed pipe bands. But the burly men who wrestle their mighty thews, who stagger gigantically under the burden of a 'caber', who run and leap and hop-skip-and-jump, are professional strong men from the cities who compete in the hope of winning a money prize. The ridiculous young girls who dance in the kilt with their blouse fronts displaying as many medals as a retired general are the tools of ambitious mothers who take their children from one gathering to the next in the hope that maternal ambition will be solaced by yet another jingling medal.

Highland Games are part of the unreal Scotland that is regularly displayed for the wondering tourist. Many of them were originally designed to amuse the 'gentry' who came every summer to shoot the livestock in the hills and were incapable of amusing themselves otherwise. The gentry still attend the games because their names are printed in the programmes and *noblesse oblige* is an easy acquiescence in the tame orgies of muscle, music and marquees.

Some of the Games are a venue for piping, and perhaps because of this a great deal may be forgiven. Piping is an art, and, like all arts, has its select informed devotees, its idolators, and its detractors. As a public entertainment it has been pushed far beyond the bounds of artistry and the sight of a pipe-band of plump smooth-kneed young women purporting to render authentic Highland music is, to the purist, a matter of insulting sacrilege. There are, broadly, two kinds of pipe music. There is the thumping, swaggering music of the full band—pipes and drums and drum-major—and there is the music played by one man.

The pipe band, even if it is mediocre, but provided it is not feminine, is a heart-stirring propagator of martial noise. A good pipe band has an astonishing emotional quality. It summons up the blood, quickens the heart, and sets the feet moving to distant horizons. But the pipe music of a solitary player is as different from this as a concert pianist is from a trumpet and accordion band. There are perhaps fifty men who are entitled to the title 'piper'. It is they who play *ceol mor*—the big music, *piobaireachd*. It is they who carry on the tradition of piping, and they foregather at some of the Highland Games. They are head and shoulders above their fellows and there is no mistaking their greatness. The ordinary run of piping is a trivial thing in comparison. One either likes it or dislikes it. There is also the laudable and understandable point of view of Beachcomber:

Nothing is more amusing than to see an octopus playing the bagpipes. It often seems that the bagpipes are playing the octopus. And the kind of music which comes from that inextricable jumble of tentacles, chanters, drones and bags is such that nobody really cares which is playing what.

The Scots, uneasy in differentiating between sentiment and sentimentality, have developed a taste for the rose-water of romance. Bonnie Prince Charlie and Mary Queen of Scots have been so diluted by the sob-sister sorority of lady novelists that the first appears like a tailor's dummy for Highland Dress and the other has become a forlorn figurehead of beautiful wronged womanhood. It might be nearer the truth if the Bonnie Prince were described as a sulky ambitious incompetent and the Queen as a tiresome termagant. As it is there are Scottish children, so divorced in their schools from an appreciation of their history, who believe the two were husband and wife.

The preoccupation with tartan has reached such an extent that it interested Professor Toynbee in his *Study of History*:

The Scots have nearly persuaded the English, if not themselves, that the Highland tartan—which the citizens of Edinburgh A.D. 1700 regarded very much as the citizens of Boston at the same date regarded the feathered headgear of an Indian chief—is the national dress of Scotland, and the Lowland confectioners now sell 'Edinburgh Rock' in tartan covered cartons.

The mixture of tartan, hairy tweed, Aberdeen jokes, whisky bottles, stage comedians and other trivia that pinpoints Scotland in the mind of the world, is itself the product of Scotland. It is perhaps a natural degeneration in a country that lost its unique identity to such an extent that its name almost vanished and for a time it became known as North Britain. The relics of its nationhood are plundered by the pedlars of souvenirs and the designers of travel posters.

But sentimentality is an excess. It is a misunderstanding, and an explosion, of those feelings which other Scots have cultivated with a care that never becomes precious. It is the portrayal of this balance between emotion and mawkishness that informs the small masterpiece, *Beattock for Moffat*, the short story by Don Roberto (R. B. Cunningham-Graham). It is with the poetry of emotion that the Scot has excelled.

> *Ae fond kiss and then we sever,*
> *Ae fareweel, perhaps for ever.*

Robert Burns was the exemplar of the terse control of emotion. It requires genius to tread this careful path, with the slough of banality on one side and the mire of bathos on the other. C. M. Grieve (Hugh MacDiarmid) treads it frequently. Probably his most famous poem is one that is a lesson in emotional understatement. It is much anthologized:

The rose of all the world is not for me.
I want, for my part,
Only the little white rose of Scotland,
That smells sharp and sweet,
And breaks the heart.

R. L. Stevenson knew the way of the narrow path, but could not quite follow it.

Be it granted me to behold you again in dying,
Hills of home, and to hear again the call,
Hear about the graves of the martyrs the pee-wees crying,
And hear no more at all.

This emotion, this sentiment which so easily destroys itself, which is so difficult to discipline in words, is the mainspring of some of the greatest Scottish poetry. Undisciplined, it is the wash that sweeps through the columns of Glasgow's newspapers, and leaves little bits of tartan ribbon tied to picture-postcards of the Highlands, the flotsam of sentimentality.

Chapter Eighteen

ILLUSTRATION FROM THE TITLE PAGE OF VOLUME TWO,
PENNANT'S *Tour in Scotland, 1772*.

TO LOOK TO THE FUTURE

We the people of Scotland who subscribe this Engagement, declare our belief that reform in the constitution of
our country is necessary to secure good government in
accordance with our Scottish traditions and to promote the
spiritual and economic welfare of our nation.

(First paragraph of the Scottish Covenant for Home Rule,
1949.)

WHEN THE SECRETARY OF State for Scotland, in the
House of Commons, called the covenant a piece of
'emotionalism' he was not quite accurate. Had he borrowed
a phrase from contemporary fiction and called it 'romantic
realism' he would have been more exact. Romantic realism

is the strength and weakness of the Scots. It is the key to their many-sided character.

It is not the politician, looking for straws in the British wind, who profits from a study of contemporary Scottish nationalism. It is the sociologist, interested in what makes a people tick. Scotland is a fascinating case-history, a miniature but complete working model of moods and enthusiasms, ambitions and policies, expressed as a national outlook.

The country lost its royal court in the seventeenth century. It lost its parliament a hundred years later. Contemporary nationalism—which might more accurately be described as patriotism—draws a lot of its sustenance from history. It implies the difference of the Scots from their neighbours and it asserts an historic right to function as a nation. Psychologically it might be the attitude of a younger brother towards his older and more powerful sibling. For the Scot, independent though he is by character, has the feeling that historically, he lost out on a family bargain. The union between Scotland and England was one-sided in its favours.

The nationalist maintains that the political merger of the two countries was not a success. He will take a point in history such as the depopulation of the Highlands and wed it with a point of modern fact, such as the high death rate from social disease in Scotland's industrial belt. From these he produces an argument that Scotland, once a small independent nation, is now no more than the confused neglected remnant of a people. He wishes, he says, to rebuild his country.

The moderate nationalist, the type of person who signed the covenant, is not a person of extreme views. He insists most scrupulously that he is not 'against England'. He is 'for

Scotland'. Demands for home-rule have been made in Scotland at various times since the end of last century. The obvious hurdle is that the necessary legislation has to be passed by the British parliament, where Scottish representatives are in a minority. In the 1880's the home-rule policy was formulated within the ranks of the Scottish Labour movement, then being organized by Keir Hardie. It was an echo of this that reached Gladstone's ear when Lord Rosebery informed him that 'the words home-rule have begun to be distinctly and loudly mentioned in Scotland'.

The modern development of Scottish nationalism began after the First World War when the demand for home-rule grew out of its party confines and took a more comprehensive setting. The twenties saw a cultural-political revival. Home-rule had a popular international flavour. It was part of the idea of a grouping of small independent states under an international body such as the League of Nations. At that time Compton Mackenzie said that

no special case for the practical expression of Scottish nationalism can be presently adequate until it is grasped that the movement in Scotland is part of an impulse everywhere perceptible to obstruct the contrary tendency, which would substitute for the diversified individual standardized groups.

In 1934, when Scottish hunger-marchers went to London, the Scottish Clydesdale Bank said it was 'unfortunate that so much depends on forces over which Scotsmen as such have little control. Her native resources are great.' It was an Englishman, Sir William Goodchild, acting as chairman of the Scottish Economic Committee, who described Scotland as 'dragged at the tail of the English chariot'. Mr William Power, author and editor, wrote in the same year (1934) that

'there has come an awakening and a new hope for Scotland
. . . the Scotland of the future will be the Scotland of the
Scots.'

Year by year more people turned to the new idea of home-
rule. A dynamic of great force was necessary to release, in all
spheres of activity, a nationalism that had been quiescent for
two hundred years and which most people might reasonably
have expected to become extinct. The dynamic was such
that it cut across the hatred of party politics and the preju-
dices of class. It united in outlook men of leisured wealth
with the hunger marchers. It joined the kilted gentry with
the Clydeside communists. The dynamic was poverty, slums,
misery, unemployment, on a scale that England had never
known. The two ends of Britain were poles apart.

This disparity between Scotland and England, still obvious
after the war against Hitler, is one of the fundamental arguments of the Scottish nationalist. Scottish housing needs are
five to seven times worse than those of England. The legacy
of slums is appalling. Professor Dewar Gibb of Glasgow
wrote in 1950, 'The simple truth is that such places should
not exist in a civilized country. Not a few swine live better
than the men and women who inhabit them.' Overcrowd-
ing, bad housing, unemployment, malnutrition have brought
a terrible toll of death. The death incidence varies so exactly
with social conditions that in one Glasgow district there was
an infant mortality rate of sixty-three per thousand. Round
the corner, in streets of better-class houses, the rate dropped
to twenty-eight.

Such conditions provide an explanation of the vast
numbers who leave Scotland annually. Emigration is a
hæmorrhage that saps the best blood of the country. During

the ten years 1921–31, 393,000 people left Scotland. That was nearly one-twelfth of the total population. In 1951 emigration continues at an excessive rate.

There, says the nationalist, are my arguments for home-rule. They are arguments of mid-twentieth century. They are not sentimental, they are not emotional, they are the hard arguments of economic and social need.

Allied with the rise of nationalism was the cultural revival of the nineteen-twenties. Until Hugh MacDiarmid wrote his early lyrics and enunciated his Scottish programme the country, on the creative plane, had been a desert of mediocrity since the days of Robert Burns and Walter Scott. The few exceptional men such as Robert Louis Stevenson could not light the gloom of Scotland's spirit. The land had decayed into the sentimentality of drunk Scotch comedians. Every young man of talent went south to London or abroad. There was no room for him at home.

To the younger generation who learned from him, MacDiarmid has been a revelation, almost an act of God. His influence in irrigating the desert of Scottish art and letters has been acutely observed in other countries. Since the twenties the atmosphere of suet-pudding and the shorter catechism has vanished. Eric Linklater writes of 'confidence, high spirits, appetite, and intellect'. MacDiarmid's contemporaries, Linklater himself, Neil Gunn, Compton Mackenzie, the late James Bridie, Edwin Muir, are part of the change that has come over Scotland, though they are not themselves intense preaching nationalists.

MacDiarmid injected enthusiasm into young Scots languishing in the doldrums of a country that had lost itself. To his followers he *is* Scotland, a flesh and blood emanation of a country's imaginative will. His peculiar recipe is a mixture of dialectical materialism, anthropological patriotism, and poetic vision.

MacDiarmid is an extremist. He expresses the national ethos in his own adamant and uncompromising way. Of the many who have been influenced by him there are few who completely share his views. He has been a liberating force rather than an exact teacher.

In 1935, a book was published in London by the Scottish author, John Connell. It was called *David Go Back* and it portrayed, in fiction that approached melodrama, the feeling and sentiments behind Scottish nationalism. The fantastic story was a frame for a sharp picture of Scottishness.

The hero of the book leads an abortive revolt to 'liberate' Scotland. In the end he is captured and sentenced to death at the Old Bailey. 'Have you anything to say before sentence is passed on you?' asks the judge. There follows a short speech which condenses into a few lines the groping emotional cry for personal liberty within national freedom:

Not in being wealthy, or having great industries, or vast political power, is a country free. A country may be poor and weak and friendless; but in the spirit of her men and women is her chance for freedom. I wanted to create that spirit again. I wanted men to believe that Scotland was worth living for, worth fighting for, worth dying for: not your flabby British Empire, and your pot-bellied commercial jingoism, but small, poverty-stricken, bitter, unhappy, pious Scotland.

There one finds an expression of Scottish nationalism— not really a nationalism at all, but a study in puritanism and emotionalism, and above all a study in freedom. It is the defiance of a small community towards the standardization imposed by the great powers of the world. It is a refutation of the rule of the big battalions. It is individual man, shaking off the threats, cajolements and bribes of his fellows, and quoting with an almost naïve impertinence 'To thine own self be true'. Whether or not one agrees with the ramifications of Scottish nationalism in other directions, with the confusion of implications that it has acquired in the middle of the century, in the middle of world upheavals, whether or not one thinks a parliament in Scotland is a sound proposition, there remains the inner kernel expressing personal liberty in the true tradition of western humanism, and in direct descent from the Declaration of Arbroath in the fourteenth century.

Out of the past—out of the achievements of Duns Scotus, Thomas the Rhymer, Barbour, Henryson, Duncan Ban Macintyre, Ramsay, Burns, Raeburn, Hume, Hutton, Scott, Jeffrey, Telford, Clerk Maxwell, Watt, Frazer, D'Arcy Thomson—there arises a confidence that the country has still much to give to civilization. In the words of the Scots proverb, 'What maun be, maun be'.